166

THE SHAAR PRESS

THE JUDAICA IMPRINT
FOR THOUGHTFUL PEOPLE

A SHAAR PRESS PUBLICATION

Light at the End of the Tunnel

an inspirational story by

RABBI ABRAHAM J. TWERSKI, M.D.

Published by **SHAAR PRESS**
Distributed by MESORAH PUBLICATIONS, LTD.
4401 Second Avenue / Brooklyn, N.Y 11232 / (718) 921-9000

Distributed in Israel by SIFRIATI / A. GITLER
6 Hayarkon Street / Bnei Brak 51127

Distributed in Europe by LEHMANNS
Unit E, Viking Industrial Park, Rolling Mill Road / Jarrow, Tyne and Wear, NE32 3DP/ England

Distributed in Australia and New Zealand by GOLDS WORLD OF JUDAICA
3-13 William Street / Balaclava, Melbourne 3183 / Victoria Australia

Distributed in South Africa by KOLLEL BOOKSHOP
Shop 8A Norwood Hypermarket / Norwood 2196, Johannesburg, South Africa

ISBN: 1-57819-705-8 Hard Cover
ISBN: 1-57819-706-6 Paperback

Printed in the United States of America by Noble Book Press
Custom bound by Sefercraft, Inc. / 4401 Second Avenue / Brooklyn N.Y. 11232

Introduction

There are things that we may know, but our intellectual knowledge may not have much effect on our behavior. Becoming accustomed to something may lull one into complacency and traveling the road of life while in this state is like being lulled into somnolence. This is comparable to highway hypnosis, where falling asleep at the wheel is extremely dangerous. But then something occurs which breaks through the complacency, making us aware of things to which we have been oblivious. This abrupt, generally unforeseen experience gives us an emotional as well as an intellectual understanding, and it is then that the knowledge impacts on what we think and what we do. In the absence of such incidents one may plod through what appears to be a normal, even a fulfilling life, because it indeed complies with the cultural norms.

One winter, *knowing* that there were ice patches on the sidewalk, I ventured out of doors with caution. Inasmuch as I slipped and fell, I obviously had not been careful enough. As a result of the painful bruises I sustained, I walked *much more carefully.*

Was there really any difference in my knowledge that there were slippery spots on the sidewalk? I think not. Then why was I more careful than before the fall? Because now that knowledge had been reinforced and made qualitatively different by the emotion of pain.

There is much talk about spirituality, and spirituality is believed to indeed be of utmost importance. Yet, many people may go through an entire lifetime without truly implementing spirituality in their lives. Especially in a culture where spirituality is often a distant second to the pursuit of pleasure, complacency about one's spirituality is commonplace.

The following story relates one man's journey that was initiated by an intense emotional experience. It is my hope and prayer that we may strive toward spirituality because we recognize its importance, and that we may be spared from the need to be aroused from our complacency by harsh experiences.

Light at the End of the Tunnel

"If you're asking whether there is light at the end of the tunnel, I must frankly say that I don't know." Those were the doctor's words.

It had all begun so innocently. I had a nagging cough that had persisted for three weeks and had not improved with cough medicine. My wife, Evelyn, insisted that I consult our family physician. "Ridiculous," I said. "It'll go away by itself. I once had a cough that lasted for six weeks." But there was no arguing with Evelyn, so I made an appointment with Dr. Berman.

Dr. Berman's examination was more thorough than usual. "Let's take a blood test and a chest X-ray," he said. "We do them right here in the office."

After a long half-hour wait, Dr. Berman called me into his office. "Alan," he said, "this is not just an ordinary cough. I'm concerned about the blood test and the chest X-ray. In fact, you must go directly from here to the hospital for several days."

I was stunned. "You've got to be kidding," I said.

"I don't kid about such things, Alan. I don't like to be an alarmist, but this is something that must be carefully evaluated. I've called the hospital and arranged for your admission."

"But I can't . . . " I sputtered. "I mean, the office, and what about Evelyn?"

"I've taken the liberty of calling Evelyn. She will meet you at the hospital. As for the office, you understand that your health has priority."

I left Dr. Berman's office in a daze. What could be wrong? I never smoked, so it couldn't be lung cancer. What in the world is Dr. Berman so concerned about? Except for the cough, I felt fine. Do I tire more easily? Perhaps. But at fifty-four I don't have the stamina I had at forty. So what?

How I drove to the hospital, especially through rush-hour traffic, I don't know. How can you drive after a ten ton load suddenly hit you in the head? In spite of my trust in Dr. Berman, I might have set the whole thing aside, except that he told me that Evelyn was on her way to the hospital.

Evelyn was in the hospital lobby when I arrived. She obviously had been crying. "What's the matter with you?" I said. "There's nothing wrong with me. I feel fine. Dr. Berman just wants to do some tests." Evelyn forced a smile. "I know you'll be alright," she said, fighting back tears.

In the evening, Dr. Berman came. "I'm having Dr. Harriman, the oncologist, see you tomorrow and order the tests," he said.

"Oncologist?" I said. "That's a cancer specialist. What in the world are you talking about? I don't have cancer."

"Look, Alan," Dr. Berman said. "Your blood count and chest x-ray are very suggestive of a malignancy. Fortunately, it looks like the lymphoma type, which is very responsive to treatment. I think you can have an excellent result, but we can't fool around. We'll know more precisely after Dr. Harriman finishes his testing."

Dr. Harriman came the following morning. The next two days were tests and more tests. Blood tests, x-rays, MRI, bone marrow biopsy and a few more. Sitting in the X-ray room was traumatic. I was clad in a flimsy gown, waiting my turn with other patients, waiting for someone to call my name.

This was preposterous! My mortality and frailty suddenly hit me. I was a pillar of strength, the managing partner in a major law firm. I stood toe to toe in court with major multinational corporations, and held my own with the best of them. What in heaven's name was I doing in a flimsy gown that barely covered me? This was absurd. A nightmare, a bad dream, that's what it was. I was going to wake up and be relieved to find it was only a dream.

But it wasn't a dream. It was stark reality. A reality that I had never previously experienced.

I had to put up with my daughter, Adina. She is a sweet child, and no father has a more devoted daughter. But somehow she had become an advocate of "natural" holistic medicine and had little use for conservative medicine. When Marvin was a baby and had an ear infection, she did not consult a doctor for antibiotics, but instead used garlic ear drops.

Adina was opposed to my undergoing conventional medical treatment. "Those medications they use are poisons," she said. She brought me literature with testimonials of people who were cured of cancer with diet and herbal remedies. I did not want to offend my child, and it took all of my wizardry to keep her at bay.

Rabbi Segal dropped by. He is a very sensitive and caring person. I had not had too much contact with him. Religion was not my forte. I went to synagogue for my parents' *yahrzeit*, for Rosh Hashanah and Yom Kippur, and to attend Bar-Mitzvahs and weddings of my friends' children. We kept our home kosher out of respect for Evelyn's parents, but that's about the scope of it.

Rabbi Segal asked for my Hebrew name and my mother's name. Avraham is my name, and my mother was Chana Glickel. He said they would say a prayer for me at the Torah, which was fine with me. Rabbi Segal had never tried to push religion on me. Before he left, he handed me a little booklet. "You may find it helpful," he said. I thanked him and made a mental note to send a contribution to the synagogue.

Dr. Harriman came one evening to give me his conclusions. I tried to read his face, but he was straightforward and unemotional. In contrast to Dr. Berman, who was a lifelong friend and called me Alan, Dr. Harriman addressed me as Mr. Silverman.

"Mr. Silverman," he said, "you have a condition known as non-Hodgkins lymphoma. It has probably been with you for some time, but it generally does not show symptoms. It is in a fairly advanced stage. It is in your chest, which is why you were coughing. It is also in your bone marrow.

"There is treatment for this disease, which consists of chemotherapy. This does not require hospitalization. It can be done at my office. There are, or course, some uncomfortable side-effects. I'm going to leave you some literature about the chemotherapy. After you've read it, I'll be glad to answer any questions, so feel free to call me. Your first treatment is scheduled for Monday at my office."

I knew I needed to ask the question, but the words just didn't come out. What I did say was, "Does chemotherapy cure this disease?"

"We don't use the word 'cure.' We speak of 'remission.' Treatment can bring the disease under control, and you will be able to carry on normal living. There may be recurrences, which will require additional treatment."

"But, Dr. Harriman, I mean, you know, I am fifty-four. I head a major law firm, and . . . "

That's when Dr. Harriman spoke the words with which I began my story: "If you're asking whether there is light at the end of the tunnel, I must frankly say that I don't know. There is ongoing research in this field. Perhaps we may be able to one day say 'cure.' " And with that, he shook my hand and left.

I was glad Evelyn was not there at the time. I broke down and cried. I had not cried since I was six years old, when I fell off my bike. Crying was for sissies. I was a man, even as a child, let alone as a prominent, powerful attorney. Everything just hit me at once. I had lost control of my life. The doctors were now my masters, and I had to be the obedient servant, as it were. Every day of my professional life, I had called the shots. Now they were going to call the shots. And I had to sit in the flimsy gown, with the nurses talking to me as though I were a dim-witted three-year-old. It still had not fully sunk in. It still felt like a nightmare from which I would soon awaken and go to the office.

I leafed through Dr. Harriman's pamphlet. I would receive intravenous medication, which might cause nausea and mouth sores. Its function was to suppress the growth of malignant cells, but it does not discriminate, and it may also suppress growth of healthy cells, particularly the white blood cells that fight infection. If the white blood cells were severely depressed, I might require hospitalization for a few days to avoid massive infection. I put the pamphlet down. I'd had enough bad news.

I picked up Rabbi Segal's booklet. It discussed the healing powers of God and prayer. I thought, "If God can heal disease, why doesn't He just prevent it in the first place?" Then I thought, "Well, perhaps He wasn't too happy with me. I really never had much to do with Him." I was Bar-Mitzva-hed and learned how to put on *tefillin*, which I only did when I observed my parents' *yahrzeit* in the synagogue. I felt guilty that I had not personally said *kaddish* for them. But how could I? I was at the office at 7:30 in the morning, and I certainly could not get away for afternoon services. I engaged someone to say the *kaddish* for me. Maybe I should have done so myself.

They say that there are no atheists in a foxhole. I never was an atheist. I always believed in God. It's just that He never occupied a significant place in my life.

But I couldn't really blame my disease on my lack of attention to religion. Our cantor, Rev. Goldschmidt, was a paragon of religion. His life was totally absorbed in God and in religious observance, yet he died of cancer of the pancreas at fifty-seven. God could not have been displeased with him.

For a moment the thought flashed through my mind that perhaps I should take religion more seriously, but I soon dismissed that. Dr. Harriman said that I would be able to function normally. There was no reason to make any change in my lifestyle.

I read a few psalms in Rabbi Segal's booklet. Then there was the prayer for the sick, in which one prayed for "healing of the spirit and healing of the body." Healing of the spirit? In what way was my spirit sick? Why did it need healing? And how did one go about healing a spirit?

I put the booklet down and turned on the TV. There was a sitcom which was supposed to be humorous. The audience was laughing, but it did not seem funny to me. Strange. I had laughed at similar jokes in the past, but now they seemed inane. I clicked the remote control and watched two innings of a ballgame. I called Evelyn to say goodnight. She was going to pick me up in the morning. I rang for the nurse to bring me my sleeping pill.

I arrived home to a homecoming party that would have done justice to a team that had won the Super Bowl. Adina and her husband were there, and they had kept Marvin out of school for the gala event. The thought flashed through my mind, "Marvin is nine. Will I be at his Bar-Mitzvah? Is the tunnel four years long?" But my attention was quickly diverted. My younger daughter, Hadassah, had taken off from work. There were brightly colored balloons. "Get well, quickly!" and "We love you," and "Welcome home." Everybody was in a festive mood, and it felt good.

One of my senior partners in the firm was there, too. Oscar and I had been friends since law school. He had visited me in the hospital and had reassured me that everything in the office was being taken care of. He had had an important deposition postponed till the following week.

We drank *L'Chaim* to my health. I kissed my children and told them how happy they had made me. Then I said, "O.K. everyone. Back to school, back to work, including me." Evelyn tried to discourage me from going to the office, but it was no use. I agreed to wait until after lunch, but that was all.

I received a hero's welcome at the office from all the staff. Just no balloons.

I was going through the mail from the past few days when Oscar came in. He sat down and said, "Alan, you know that as lawyers we have to follow the advice we give our clients. You may live to be a hundred, but it is really important to review things and see that everything is in order."

Of course, I knew what he meant, and he was right. Eight years ago I had made a will, which was *pro forma*, and it hadn't bothered me a bit. But this time it was different. I felt a sting. Eight years ago I did not think of tunnels, but now I could not be sure there was light at the end of the tunnel. There could be recurrences, low blood count, massive infections. We were playing hardball.

I gulped. "Yeah, of course," I said. "Ask Mark to get my old will out of the files. He helped me draft it."

Mark was a bright young man who dealt with wills and estate planning. We spent two hours updating the will. I also made a living will. If I ever reached a vegetative stage I saw no reason to prolong my existence.

Mark was my protégé. He was probably the son I never had. When we had wrapped up everything, he still hung around. I am not stupid. "What's on your mind, Mark? I think we've covered all the bases. What's bugging you?"

Mark spoke like he had a hot potato in his mouth. "If you've made a living will, you're not denying the fact that you may . . . Oh, what the heck! We all have to die someday. Have you provided for a cemetery plot?"

Cemetery! That's for dead people! Again, the nightmare wish. Mark became bleary eyed. "I'm sorry, Alan," he said. "But you know, we've . . . "

"Of course, of course," I said. "No, I had not thought of

that. But you're right. One day I'll need it. I'll look into it."

I walked out of the office building to the parking garage across the street. Rush hour was at its peak: cars weaving in and out of traffic, impatient drivers tooting their horns, pedestrians hurrying across the street, deftly dodging cars. I paused. What's the matter with these people? Everyone hurrying to get somewhere ten seconds faster? What for? They're not going to live forever either. Do they think about where they are going, or are they so absorbed in getting there faster that they don't even think about the significance of their destination? No doubt, they think that whatever it is they happen to be pursuing is of momentous importance. Actually, these things may be quite insignificant.

But why am I critical of them? I was no different just several days ago. Everything I was doing was of momentous importance, but now all of that has faded into insignificance. What is now foremost in my mind is, will I be at Marvin's Bar-Mitzvah? I would so like to live to see Hadassah happily married. Amazing how our values can change.

My trip home required driving through a tunnel. I thought of Dr. Harriman's words. This tunnel was about a mile long, and within a few seconds I could see the light at the end of the tunnel. I could not help but wonder whether there was any light at the end of my tunnel.

At dinner, I told Evelyn that Rabbi Segal had visited me at the hospital and that I wanted to make a contribution to the synagogue. "I think I'll take it to him personally. I appreciated his visit."

R abbi Segal appeared genuinely happy to see me. "Much better that you come to me than I come to visit you," he said. "And so, what did the doctors find?"

I told Rabbi Segal about the diagnosis and the rather ominous-sounding prognosis. He said, "The Talmud states that a person is obligated to seek medical help. One might think, 'If God causes a person to be ill, then man should not interfere with His plans.' Not so, says the Talmud. It derives the physician's authority to treat diseases from a passage in the Torah.

"But the Torah only authorizes a physician to treat. It does not authorize a doctor to set limits on how long a person can live. That is God's prerogative."

I nodded assent, then said, "I want to consult you on another matter. I don't like to think of it. We know that no one lives forever and that one should prepare for the inevitable. But when the inevitable appears not to be too far away, it takes on a different character.

"I do not have any cemetery plot," I said. "You know, my

parents are buried in the shul cemetery, and it is only logical that I be near them. How do I go about making arrangements?''

"You are very wise," Rabbi Segal said. "You've just done something to increase your longevity. Preparing one's burial place is a *segulah* for long life."

"What is a *segulah*?" I asked.

"The closest I can come to it is a 'good luck charm.' There is a tradition that making arrangements for one's burial brings a blessing for long life.

"Actually," Rabbi Segal said, "I don't like to think of this tradition in terms of a *segulah*. I think it has a more substantial meaning. People who give no serious thought to life on earth being transitory tend to be totally preoccupied with earthly achievements. They may lead a frenetic life, trying to increase their wealth and possessions. The pressure and stresses of this lifestyle may place a strain on the heart and make them more vulnerable to heart attack or other stress diseases.

"People who prepare for their burial are more apt to think of life in different terms. They may realize that there is more to one's life than making money or achieving prominence. They are less likely to lead a frenetic life."

As if he read my mind, Rabbi Segal said, "When we pray for a sick person, we ask that God grant him a *refuas hanefesh*, healing of the spirit, and *refuas haguf*, healing of the body. We ask for healing of the spirit first, because a healthy spirit is conducive to healing of the body. A person with a healthy spirit has greater trust in God. He is less worried, less agitated. I've been told that there is scientific research that demonstrates the effect of attitude toward recovery from illness."

I said, "I was thinking about that when I read the pamphlet you left for me. One day we should discuss what spiritual healing is all about."

Rabbi Segal saw that I was not interested in pursuing the subject at this time. "Regarding your inquiry about the cemetery," he said, "call Arnold Fineman. He is in charge of the cemetery. And remember, it is a *segulah* for long life."

The chemotherapy did not turn out to be as formidable as I had feared. I was able to keep pace at the office, although on several occasions I left early because I tired easily. We were into serious litigation, and my intense involvement in work actually diverted my attention from the nausea. Repeat tests were favorable, and Dr. Harriman was pleased with the results.

The letter from the shul asking whether I wished to reserve my seats for the High Holidays was accompanied by an announcement of Rabbi Segal's pre-High Holidays series of lectures. Although I had not attended any of these in the past, I thought I would sit in on one of them now. Evelyn said she would join me.

Rabbi Segal spoke about preparing ourselves for Rosh Hashanah with *teshuvah,* or rectifying our lives. On Rosh Hashanah we ask God to inscribe us for another year of life. Whereas God determines the quantity of our days, He does not determine their quality. Every person is a free agent to choose to live according to God's will or to digress from it.

Rosh Hashanah is followed by Yom Kippur, the day of forgiveness. Rabbi Segal said that Yom Kippur is generally thought of as an amnesty, wherein all of a person's sins are forgiven, unless, that is, one sinned against another person, in which case God does not forgive unless one has set things straight with whomever one had offended.

Rabbi Segal raised a question: inasmuch as Rosh Hashanah is a new beginning, it is only logical to start off the new year with a clean slate. One would think that the sequence should be reversed; i.e., that Yom Kippur should come first so that all sins are forgiven, and *then* Rosh Hashanah should begin the new year.

Rabbi Segal explained that Yom Kippur is really not a blanket amnesty, and that a person must contribute something toward attaining forgiveness. True, we sacrifice something by not eating, but that is hardly enough to warrant forgiveness for errant behavior. What is necessary is a commitment to proper living, which can only come about by an awareness of what is expected of a person.

It is generally assumed, Rabbi Segal said, that Rosh Hashanah celebrates Creation, and that the world came into being on the first day of Tishrei. Indeed, in the Rosh Hashanah services we say, "Today is the birth[day] of the world." However, the Midrash says that Rosh Hashanah is the day on which Adam was created; i.e., the sixth day of creation in the account in Genesis.

Man came into a world that was designed for him to fulfill his mission. Man is the crown jewel of creation, superior to everything that came before him. Man is superior not only to all living things, but also to angels. Both animals and angels were created in a state of completion. Angels never change, and animals grow only in size and mass. Man was created as a potential with unique capabilities which he must develop. If man fails to develop all his uniquely human capabilities, he is derelict in his humanity, and to the degree that he neglects their development, he is actually animal-like.

Animals do not sin. They have no obligation to act responsibly. They do not need to be forgiven. A lion which kills for food is not a murderer, whereas a man who kills out of anger is a criminal. Why? Because man has the capacity to control his anger.

At this point, Evelyn looked at me and we exchanged smiles. Evelyn and I have a good marriage, which was marred only by my occasional outbursts of anger. I do have a vitriolic temper, and I can be extremely offensive when I lose control. Evelyn had suggested that I see a psychologist for anger management, but I thought this was unnecessary. I had enough will power to be in control of my anger, or so I thought. Obviously, my will power had not been completely effective.

Rabbi Segal continued by stating that forgiveness cannot come until a person accepts responsibility for his behavior. Rosh Hashanah represents the creation of man as a unique creature, and it is this awareness and acceptance of responsibility that must precede the forgiveness of Yom Kippur.

Rabbi Segal cited the Torah that when God created man, "He blew a breath of life into his nostrils." God breathed something from within Himself into man, and this something is the *neshamah*, the human soul, which is Godly. The human soul, like God, is eternal. When a person's life on earth is over, it is only his physical component that dies, but his soul lives on.

I looked at Evelyn, but she avoided eye contact. She knew I would be reacting to this idea.

I had never given any thought to this subject. From childhood on, I was too busy doing things that "mattered" to contemplate matters like the soul. Certainly as an adult, I was totally engrossed in practical issues, and the idea of a soul never entered my mind. I guess we are deluded to think of ourselves as eternal in a physical sense. Many people, including myself, act as though we are going to live forever. My disease had made me more conscious of my mortality. I had updated my will and had contacted Arnold Fineman to purchase burial plots for myself and Evelyn, but I had not thought of any kind of existence after death, that there was part of me that would not go out of existence.

The idea that there was part of me that would survive should have been comforting, but at that particular moment it had no soothing effect. *Neshamah* was just a word. I could not relate to it as a real entity.

After the lecture I told Rabbi Segal that I would be interested in reading something about *neshamah,* and he said he would give me a list of books.

6

Evelyn's parents and her brother and sister-in-law came for Rosh Hashanah. They are really sweet people. It had been some time since we had spent a holiday together. We had a great time. Being together with family can be enriching as well as enjoyable. I wondered why we had not gotten together more often. For me, being with family at this time was very supportive.

I did concentrate more on the Rosh Hashanah prayers, especially those asking to be inscribed in the Book of Life. I noted that on Rosh Hashanah it is decided, "Who shall live and who shall die," and that *teshuvah* (repentance), prayer, and *tzedakah* (charity) can revoke an unfavorable decree. I was praying more, and was contributing to *tzedakah*. As for repentance, well, I wasn't sure I had that much need to repent. I felt I was leading a very decent life.

After services, Rabbi Segal asked whether Evelyn and I would join him for a meal in his succah. Succah! I hadn't been in a succah since I was a kid. My Zeide had a succah, and I must have been seven or eight when I watched him put together a succah from some paneling he had in his garage. I had helped him decorate the succah. That was fun. We ate in the succah a few times. Zeide died later that year, and I was never in a succah since. I gladly accepted Rabbi Segal's invitation. He also suggested that I check with my doctor whether my condition allowed me to fast on Yom Kippur. That was very thoughtful of him. I did fast on Yom Kippur, except for a few sips of water to swallow some medication.

On Yom Kippur, Rabbi Segal delivered a sermon on *teshuvah*. He said that some people may feel that they did no wrong and that they had nothing to repent. I thought he was talking about me. Rabbi Segal pointed out that a person has an obligation to perfect himself spiritually. He quoted from Psalms, "Desist from evil and do good." It is not enough to abstain from doing wrong. Unless one promotes oneself spiritually, one is derelict in fulfilling one's obligation, and this must be rectified.

Evelyn and I joined Rabbi Segal on the first night of the Succos festival. He had a huge succah, beautifully decorated. In addition to his family, there were three other couples. The rabbi's wife was an excellent cook, and the food was delicious.

Rabbi Segal explained that the four walls of the succah represented the miraculous Clouds of Glory which surrounded and protected the Israelites following their deliverance from Egypt. He cited the Torah, which refers to the holiday as "the festival of harvest." In ancient Israel, the Succos festival followed the gathering of the autumn harvest. It was a happy holiday, when people rejoiced upon bringing in abundant crops. He said there was also a tradition that the souls of the Patriarchs Abraham, Isaac, and Jacob come to visit the succah and bless their descendants. I liked that idea.

During the meal, Rabbi Segal and his children sang some lilting melodies, and we clapped our hands and joined the singing. Several times, he dropped brief nuggets about the succah. Then he went on to present another symbolism.

The succah, Rabbi Segal said, is a temporary dwelling. It represents man's temporary existence in the physical world, the seven days corresponding to the seven decades of the average life span. For that reason, according to Jewish law, the succah must be constructed so that it is only a temporary structure. Our permanent dwelling is in heaven. Prior to our descent to earth, our souls were in the permanent home to which they return when life is over. Symbolically, we leave our permanent home to enter a temporary structure, returning to the permanent home when the seven days (seven decades) are over.

More than all other festivals, Rabbi Segal said, Succos is celebrated with the greatest joy. If all there were to one's existence was the temporary sojourn on earth, this would be quite depressing, particularly because very few people have a totally blissful life. We all experience a variety of hardships, and many people may experience severe suffering. If our existence ended with physical death, life would be a dreary ordeal for most people. It is precisely because we can recognize our earthly existence as being temporary, with a return to our permanent home in heaven, that we can rejoice even when we are subjected to the distresses of life. That is why Succos is a joyous festival.

Although the harvest season refers to bringing in the crops from the field, we can also think of a spiritual harvest, when one returns to the permanent home with an abundant "crop" of meritorious deeds one has accomplished in his lifetime. This is bringing in the spiritual harvest.

Rabbi Segal related the story of a wealthy businessman who visited a *tzaddik* and was appalled at the *tzaddik's* dwelling. He lived in a sparsely furnished single room, where he ate and slept. He offered the *tzaddik* money to obtain better quarters.

"And you," the *tzaddik* asked, "do you live in more than one room?"

"Of course," the wealthy man answered. "I have a spacious home, with a living room, dining room, kitchen, several bed-rooms, and a study."

"And when you travel for business, do you also reside in a home with many rooms?" the *tzaddik* asked.

"No," the man said. "When I travel on business I stay in a single room in a hotel."

"That is the same with me," the tzaddik said. "My permanent home is beautiful, spacious, and furnished in great splendor. I am here on earth for a short while for business, to acquire provisions for my existence in my permanent home. Just like you, when I am away from home, I live in a single room."

A few more people joined us in the succah for dessert. When the meal was over, there was some more lively singing, and Rabbi Segal asked us to join him in dancing. The men danced in a circle and the women danced separately.

I could understand philosophically resigning oneself to one's mortality and the inevitability of death. What other choice is there? But to be *happy* about being mortal and to joyously celebrate the ephemeral nature of life was something truly novel. I had never thought of it this way.

We were dancing in the temporary structure which would be dismantled in a week. I was much more at ease when we left for home. I told Evelyn that next year we might have a succah in our home. Marvin will help me decorate it, just as I did with my Zeide.

That night in Rabbi Segal's succah had made an impression on me. My mood became more upbeat. I appeared to have responded very well to treatment.

I must confess something that I had not shared with Evelyn. I drove to and from the office via a circuitous route in order to avoid going through the tunnel. It always reminded me of Dr. Harriman's ambivilance that there might not be a light at the end of tunnel, and it may me feel gloomy. Even with my apparent successful response to treatment, I had been forewarned that this was a "remission" rather than a cure. Although I had a full schedule at the office, I had one of the other lawyers take care of out-of-town appointments. I did not feel comfortable being away from my doctors.

One of my clients died of a heart attack at age sixty-four. He had been a wealthy real estate developer who had employed my firm to take care of his legal requirements, which were many. We had also represented him in a messy divorce. I did not handle his affairs personally, but I had known him socially for some time, even before he struck it rich. Whenever he came to the office, he would stop off to say hello and exchange a few words.

I was not especially close with Henry. No one was close with Henry, not even his family. He was a cold fish whose sole purpose in life was to make more money. He owned several shopping centers and high-rise apartment buildings, but he never had enough. Had Henry lived to ten times sixty-four, he could not have exhausted his money. With Henry it was not *having* money that was important, but the thrill of *making* money. He would get a "high" out of a successful venture, and I think the high was even better if he outsmarted a competitor. Henry was a shrewd businessman. He never actually violated the law, but he had the business ethics of a rapacious tiger. Henry was not known for his charity, but he did endow a wing of the new Mount Sinai Hospital, which prominently proclaimed his beneficence as the "Henry Forman Wing."

Was Henry happy? Not between business triumphs. It was little wonder that his marriage fell apart. He was not abusive to Ethel, but she could not continue to live with an insensitive robot. The divorce was messy because Henry was in no way ready to part with what Ethel demanded. He was not in contention with his wife, the person with whom he had shared many years and who was the mother of his children, but rather with an adversary whom he had to defeat. The lawyer who represented him was thoroughly disgusted with him.

Henry had two sons and a son-in-law, all employed in his empire. They feared him rather than loved him. The two brothers were not on speaking terms. One son, Bertrand, and the son-in-law, Fred, were aggressive in the business, whereas the other son, Jack, was a happy-go-lucky who came to the office when it so pleased him. Bertrand's wife had turned the brother and sister against Jack. She was furious that this lazy lout who rarely did a stitch of work should receive a salary equal to that of her hard-working husband. Not that they ever lacked for anything, mind you. Eventually an intense hatred developed. The lazy son would not come to family affairs, or would arrive only after the other two had departed.

Jack was simply not interested in turning hundreds of millions into billions. He did not have Henry's drive. Perhaps the brother and sister were envious that Jack was the most well-liked in the community, giving freely of his wealth.

The three finally came together at Henry's funeral. I felt sorry for the rabbi who had to eulogize Henry. What was he to say about him? A warm, caring, personality who was devoted to the community? That was not Henry. A loving husband and father? That was not Henry. The poor rabbi was groping for words in front of the huge crowd assembled in the chapel, which was bedecked with flowers from the floor to the ceiling. How ironic! All those beautiful flowers, but a dearth of beautiful things to say.

I was no longer preoccupied with death. My attitude had become like the person who said, "I'm not afraid of dying. I just don't want to be there when it happens." But at Henry's funeral I could not avoid reflecting that one of these days I would be the central character in this drama. I felt comforted that the rabbi would be able to say that I was a devoted husband and father. Rabbi Segal would not be as much at a loss for what to say about me as this rabbi was with Henry.

Or would he be? What else could he say? That I built up a major law firm out of nothing? That's like praising Henry for building up a vast empire out of nothing. I thought about that, and for several days this thought nagged me.

I knew that Evelyn and the kids would miss me. It bothered me that Evelyn's memories of me might be marred by memories of my rage outbursts. "I've got to get that under control," I thought. Adina would probably pout that if I had listened to her and followed her diet and herbal treatment, I'd still be alive. Yes, Hadassah and Marvin would miss me. I had never exploded at them.

Rabbi Segal could say that I had been a happy man. But was I really? Why couldn't I relax when on vacation? Evelyn would say, "For heaven's sake, leave the cell phone at home. You can call the office once a day if you absolutely must, but you should not be answering the phone or making calls when we're relaxing at the swimming pool." I was happy only as long as I was in control of the office.

I left the chapel thinking that perhaps I should have a talk with Rabbi Segal.

8

I felt comfortable in Rabbi Segal's presence. His bright eyes sparkled with wisdom, but did not have that unnerving, penetrating quality. I had no problem in making eye contact with him. His neatly trimmed white beard made him look distinguished, but not stand-offish. Occasionally he would reach over and put his hand on mine. It was comforting.

I knew that Rabbi Segal understood suffering. He had suffered bitterly when his youngest child, a girl of eight, died of a rare disease several years earlier. He had grieved deeply but had regained his composure. When we danced in his succah, I wondered, "Had he forgotten?" It was not like him to forget. Somehow, the lingering pain did not prevent joy. I wanted to understand.

"Happiness," Rabbi Segal said, "is fulfillment. Indeed, happiness is gratification. When you are hungry, you are not very happy. When you eat, you've satisfied your need, and the unhappiness of hunger disappears.

"Of course, the gratification of satisfying your hunger is

short-lived. In a few hours the hunger recurs. But the principle is nevertheless valid. Unhappiness is the result of needs that are unsatisfied."

He continued, "Some people are not aware of their real needs. They may eat or drink in the attempt to rid themselves of discontent. But food can successfully satisfy only physical hunger. It does nothing for spiritual hunger."

Rabbi Segal paused, and I took advantage of this pause to say, "But I'm quite happy when I'm at the office."

Rabbi Segal smiled. "Yes, success and productivity at the office can provide a modicum of comfort, just like food. You have a need to produce, and that can be fulfilled. But when that relief wears off, you are driven to do more work. That is the dynamics of workaholism."

I knew he was right. That is why I had to have my cell phone at the swimming pool. I had never thought of myself as a workaholic. I rarely kept late hours, and I enjoyed several rounds of golf on Sunday morning. I did not carry my cell phone on the golf course. But of course, the office was closed Sunday mornings.

"There is that component of you, Alan, the *neshamah*, which has its own needs," Rabbi Segal said. "Neither tasty food nor even winning an important case provides the satisfaction that the *neshamah* desires. And just as the *neshamah* is eternal, the things that satisfy the *neshamah* are eternal." Rabbi Segal reached over and put his hand on mine. "You have a beautiful *neshamah*, Alan."

I don't understand why, but at that moment I had a flashback to a feeling I had had many years earlier. I was at my Zeide's, and we had just finished decorating the succah. Zeide took me into the kitchen and said to Bubby, "Give Avrumi a glass of hot chocolate. (Zeide never called me Alan, only Avrumi. I was named after his father.) It was chilly in the succah, and Avrumi worked hard." Zeide hugged and kissed me. That wonderful feeling came back when Rabbi Segal put his hand on mine. It was all I could do to keep myself from asking, "Do you have hot chocolate?" That would have turned the *déjà vu* into reality.

"I don't understand this *neshamah* thing," I said. "What is it, and how do we know it exists?"

"There are different ways of knowing things," Rabbi Segal said. "There is a story about a skeptic who came to a rabbi to learn Torah. He said he was an avowed skeptic and would never change, but that he did not want to be a skeptic out of ignorance. He wanted to learn the Torah in the original, but had never learned Hebrew.

" 'Very well,' the rabbi said. He took a Hebrew primer and pointed to a letter. 'This is an aleph,' he said.

" 'What makes you so certain that this is an aleph?' the man asked.

"The rabbi took hold of the man's ear and gave it a sharp twist. 'Ouch!' the man exclaimed. 'Let go of my ear!'

" 'What makes you so certain that this is an ear?' the rabbi asked.

" 'Everyone knows an ear is an ear,' the man said.

" 'Exactly,' the rabbi said. 'And everyone knows an aleph is an aleph.' "

"That's a cute story," I said, "but it does not address how we know the *neshamah* exists, except that many people have agreed upon it."

"There is a kind of knowledge that is based on trust. You wisely chose to undergo chemotherapy. You would not have submitted yourself to chemotherapy if you had not 'known' that it can help you. How did you know that? I'm sure that the chemical names of the medications are as meaningless to you as they are to me. You 'knew' because you had trust in your doctors. Most of your clients have scant knowledge of the law, but they essentially place their lives in your hands because they trust you, and you would never violate that trust.

"Trust is a powerful entity. The world could not function if there were no trust.

"I trust the heritage of my ancestors. We have an unbroken chain of transmission of knowledge from the time of Moses to the present. Million of Jews stood at Sinai, millions had witnessed the miracles of the Exodus, and millions received the Divine teachings that Moses conveyed. Millions of Jews did not willfully deceive their children. Children have valid reason to trust the words of their parents and grandparents, just as your clients have reason to trust you.

"It has been transmitted to us from Moses onward that God created man and endowed him with a *neshamah*. I have valid reason to trust that my father was not deceiving me, just as you know that your children have reason to trust that you would not mislead them."

"Touché!" I said. "But even if we accept the existence of the *neshamah*, that does not define it. How do we know what it is like? No one has ever seen a *neshamah*," I said.

"Nor has anyone seen gravity," Rabbi Segal said, smilingly. "Yet, no one doubts that gravity exists."

"But we can prove the existence of gravity by its visible effects," I said. "Can you do as much for the *neshamah*?"

"Perhaps we cannot do just as much," Rabbi Segal said, "but we can come close. That we have a Divine *neshamah* is a principle of faith. We can only have faith in something that cannot be absolutely proven. We do not have faith that this desk and chair exist. We can see and touch them. Faith is reserved for something that cannot be conclusively demonstrated."

I was not fully convinced. Both Rabbi Segal and I realized that we had come to the end of this particular discussion.

"I commend you for your interest," Rabbi Segal said. "Many people shun contemplation of intangibles.

"It so happens that next Thursday night I am beginning a class on spirituality. You might find it interesting," Rabbi Segal said. He handed me a book, *The Path of the Just*. "This will be our basic text . . .

"Can Evelyn come?" I asked.

"Of course," Rabbi Segal said. "It will be a rather small and intimate group, perhaps fifteen or so people. I'd love to have you and Evelyn. A week from this Thursday at 8 o'clock."

I stretched out my hand to say goodbye. Rabbi Segal took my hand between his two hands, giving it a gentle squeeze. "Shalom," he said.

The thought flashed through my mind, "When I get home I'm going to ask Evelyn to make me some hot chocolate."

T he study group consisted of eight couples. Among them were Jeff, a psychologist; Dan, a neurologist; and Howard, a musician who, of all things, played a percussion instrument in an orchestra. I had a superficial acquaintance with several of them. It promised to be a stimulating evening.

Rabbi Segal began by saying that there was an axiom that had to be stipulated. Inasmuch as the discussion is about Torah-based spirituality, it is assumed that everyone believes in the existence of God. If anyone present had questions regarding the existence of God, another study group can be organized to deal with that issue.

Rabbi Segal explained that in Judaism, God is infinite, eternal, and absolute perfection. He pointed out that "infinity" and "eternity" are words that cannot have much meaning to us, because all our information is related to sense experiences. Inasmuch as we have never come in contact with anything that was boundless in time and space, we cannot really grasp infinity nor eternity.

Inasmuch as God is absolute perfection, there cannot be any change in God. God cannot desire anything in the same way that humans desire things, because human desire indicates a lack, whereas God lacks nothing. A person who desires something is happier after his desire is satisfied. This cannot be so with God, Who does not undergo any change.

This leads to some axioms which we must accept on the basis of revelation. Logically, Creation should never have occurred. An absolutely perfect Being does not have any motivation to do anything. That God did create the universe is a matter of faith, based on revelation. We can proceed with logical reasoning only after we accept certain revealed fundamentals of faith.

The first chapter of *Path of the Just* dealt with man's obligation on earth. The author stated that the *neshamos* (souls) of human beings were in heaven, enjoying the ultimate bliss, basking in the manifest glory of God. Inasmuch as the *neshamos* had done nothing to earn this extreme delight, this pleasure was undeserved, curtailed, and incomplete. They were receiving the delight in being in God's presence as "alms," as it were, which is humiliating. The Divine goodness, therefore, decreed that the *neshamos* should come down to a physical world which is replete with temptations that entice a person to transgress God's will. By resisting temptation and loyally fulfilling God's will, the *neshamah* earns the privilege of being in God's presence, and the bliss it experiences is not flawed by being undeserved. Man's obligation on earth is, therefore, to act in a way that will merit the *neshamah* being rewarded.

Having delivered these axioms, Rabbi Segal paused, apparently to allow us to digest this. Needless to say, this huge bolus required many hours if not days to digest and absorb. "I know you have questions," he said, "so let's begin."

The psychologist spoke up. "I assume that after these

axioms are posited, we are going to develop concepts logically. We will build a logical structure on something that is incomprehensible and beyond the grasp of logic. Right?"

This was not delivered in a challenging tone. Rabbi Segal welcomed the question and said, "Psychology seeks to elucidate the mechanism of human thought and feeling. Our neurologist friend here is an expert on the brain, which is the factory where thoughts and feelings are produced. The brain is composed of billions of cells, right? These cells are composed of matter, of compounds of many chemicals. I can understand that cells can produce certain chemicals that affect other cells. But how can material substance produce thought?" Rabbi Segal turned to Dan, the neurologist. " How do you bridge the gap from physical substance to thought?" he asked.

Dan said, "We don't bridge the gap. We know which areas of the brain are related to certain sensations such as sound and sight, we know which are related to motion, and we know which parts of the brain are related to thought. If a certain area of the brain is injured, thought is impaired. But just how the brain produces thought is a mystery. Thought is a phenomenon. It is there. How matter can generate thought is not understood."

Rabbi Segal addressed Jeff, the psychologist. "Once we know that the phenomenon of thought exists, we can analyze it and try to understand how it functions, and how feelings interact with thought. But thought itself is as incomprehensible as the *neshamah*. There is actually a close parallel between spirituality as a function of the soul and psychology. The *neshamah* is a phenomenon. We may not understand its essence, but we can analyze its function."

Although I listened attentively, I was not pleased with the direction the discussion had taken. Philosophy is not my thing. I am a pragmatist, very down-to-earth. I thoroughly agreed with Sherlock Holmes who shocked Watson with his ignorance of the Copernican theory that the earth revolves around the sun rather than the reverse. Holmes added that he regretted Watson's telling him about it, and that he would now do his utmost to forget it.

"Forget it?" Watson exclaimed. "Why would you wish to forget so important a scientific discovery?"

Holmes proceeded to explain his concept of the human mind. The brain, he said, is like a cabinet with many but not an infinite number of drawers in which one can store whatever data one wishes. When all the drawers are full of data, no new data can be admitted unless one empties a drawer to make place for it. Storing data which is of no use to a person thus precludes learning and retaining data which is of value to him.

"My work is unaffected by the revolution of the sun and the earth," Holmes said. "It is of little practical difference to me which revolves around the other. Retaining useless information may impair my retention of what *is* important to me."

I was a teenager when I read *The Adventure of Sherlock Holmes,* and this made good sense to me. Philosophy 101 was a required course in college. Although I never doubted my existence, I saw the logic in the Cartesian dictum, *cogito ergo sum,* I think therefore I am. I was intrigued by Socrates' casuistry in being able to prove whatever point he wished, and after convincing someone of its validity, turn around and totally disprove it. This has served me well in my career as an attorney, when I found it necessary to convince a judge or jury that whatever I wanted them to believe was correct or factual. But the rest of philosophy served no purpose for me and I dismissed it.

I was, therefore, not interested in why God created the world. I had never doubted the existence of God and

Creation, but anything beyond that did not pique my curiosity. I essentially agreed with Dan's position that inasmuch as we cannot bridge the gap between corporeal brain and thought, we should leave the question alone and deal with the phenomenon of thought as a fact.

I was, however, extremely interested in the concept that the *neshamah* continues to exist after death. The rationale of its being deprived of unearned heavenly bliss and being sent down to endure an earthly existence where the cards were stacked against it so that it could return to where it was before was not convincing.

But even that was not important. I was still reeling from the shock of the sudden awareness of my mortality. My concept that I was the Rock of Gibraltar had been demolished. I was a frail human being who sat in the anteroom of the X-ray department clad in a flimsy gown, awaiting a picture which could predict whether I was to survive or go out of existence. The idea that there might come a time when I would never be me had never occurred to me before, but it was now a reality. The idea that there is part of me, a *neshamah*, that *would* survive was comforting. I was less interested in understanding the essence of the *neshamah* than in knowing that I would continue to exist even after I died.

Although I had not done trial work for some time, I was quite adept at convincing a jury of whatever was to my client's advantage. I had to size up the jurors and try to reason, "Why should that man or woman want to believe me?" Facts do not speak for themselves. If you do not want to know something, you can deny its reality even if it sits right in front of your face. It is a psychological fact that you believe what you want to believe. I was skilled in sizing up jurors by watching their reactions to what they heard, and thereby determining what it is that they want to believe.

I realized that the assertion that there was a *neshamah* that exists after death had struck a welcome chord. I knew that I had to be on the defensive to avoid being deluded by what I wanted to believe. I, therefore, did not try to divert the group's deliberation to a channel of my liking. I sat in silence for the rest of the session. I had some homework to do.

On the way home, I asked Evelyn what she had thought about the session. She responded that it was OK, with less enthusiasm than she would have had picking a ripe melon in the supermarket. I told her that I wished to pursue this further, but that she did not have to come along. She said she would think it over.

I realized that Evelyn did not have the same motivation that I did. Sure, she loved me and was very concerned about my health. Yet she did not experience the shattering feeling of nothingness that I did. We may talk about issues concerning death, but nothing can equal the feeling that one's existence is in jeopardy.

I remember a story about a rabbi who lost his home and entire library in a fire. He was inconsolable and grieved his loss for months. One of the congregates asked him, "You preached to us that the Talmud says we must praise God when we suffer a loss just as we do for good things." The rabbi responded, "Yes, I always understood that teaching in theory, but I have a difficult time accepting it in practice." Knowing and thinking about death is not the same as being confronted with it.

I later thought about what Evelyn would do after I was gone. She is four years younger than I am and very attractive. True, she will be well provided for and still works as a court stenographer (that's how we met), but although she will be financially comfortable, she will be lonely. She will be a good catch for anyone, and she will probably remarry, which she should do. Does a *neshamah* know what is happening in the earthly world? Will I look down (or up?) and see her being happy with another husband? Can my *neshamah* really be in bliss under such circumstances? I'll have to check this out with Rabbi Segal.

The following day I stopped at the Judaica store to see if I could find any books on the subject. There were books on spirituality that dealt with the duties of the *neshamah* in this world, but there was nothing that explained what the *neshamah* was, nor how we can come to know anything about it. There was a little book on *kaddish,* which said that when a child recites the *kaddish* for a parent, that is favorable for the parent's *neshamah.*

I began to feel very guilty that I had delegated the *kaddish* for my parents to a proxy because I was too busy at the office to attend services daily. I had had my priorities mixed up. This gnawed at me, and I felt I had to get some help from Rabbi Segal. He told me to come an hour before the next study group session.

Rabbi Segal explained that the *kaddish* is not really a memorial prayer. Not once is anything mentioned about the deceased. Rather, *yisgadal veyiskadash* means "Let the Name of God be exalted and sanctified."

"The Talmud says that we are obligated to sanctify the Name of God by behaving in a manner that will elicit the praise of God from people," Rabbi Segal said. He cited a story in the Talmud where a sage, Shimon ben Shatach, bought a mule from an Arab. In the saddle that was purchased with the mule, Shimon found a priceless gem. His disciples said, "God has blessed you with great wealth," but Shimon said, "I bought a mule. I did not buy a gem," and he returned the gem to the Arab who said, "Blessed is the God of Shimon ben Shatach."

Rabbi Segal said, "When a Jew transacts honestly and is courteous to everyone, that sanctifies the Name of God. We may not have opportunities of returning a valuable gem, but when the checkout clerk gives you too much in change and you return the excess to her, that is a sanctification of God's Name. When you go out of your way to do a *chesed* (kindness) for someone, that is a sanctification of God's Name.

"Once a person leaves the earthly world, he can no longer accrue merits. However, if he raised his children in such a way that their behavior brings honor to God's Name, that is a merit for the deceased parent. The principle of *kaddish* is to add to the deceased parent's merits by 'exalting and sanctifying' God's Name.

"It is, of course, preferable that the child of the deceased recite the *kaddish*, think of the words, and behave accordingly. Although you did not take advantage of this opportunity, you can still add to your parents' merits by behavior that will bring honor to God's Name."

I asked Rabbi Segal whether the *neshamah* knows what is happening on earth, and if so, how can a man's *neshamah* be in bliss when he sees his widow married to another man? Rabbi Segal said that it is a mistake to ascribe the emotions of a physical human being to the *neshamah*. The *neshamah* is not capable of being envious, of being angry, or of any other human emotion. The delight that the *neshamah* has being in God's radiance is totally different from any pleasurable sensation with which we are familiar.

I felt relieved that I could still compensate for my dereliction in not personally saying the *kaddish* for my parents. The bliss of the *neshamah* remained a mystery which I may never fully resolve.

When I finished my talk with Rabbi Segal, there were still twenty minutes until the study group session. I went outside to stroll around a bit.

My mind went back to *cogito ergo sum*. From what I remember, the argument went like this: Although I can see, hear, and touch my reality, I cannot be absolutely certain that things are in fact as I perceive them. Perhaps all this is only a vivid dream. In such dreams, everything seems real, until you wake up. Maybe my life is one vivid dream, a lengthy hallucination. Maybe I am even hallucinating my body. But even if everything is a hallucination, I can be absolutely certain of one thing: *I exist*! If I did not exist, I could not hallucinate. Maybe I do not exist in the form I see myself, but there is no denying that I exist.

My anxiety about death was that I would cease to exist in any way. Death may be a finality to my existence. But if my *neshamah* exists after death, then I will have an existence. As far as the form of my existence as a disembodied *neshamah* is concerned, why, I cannot be absolutely certain that I am not disembodied right at this moment! All I can know for certain now is that I exist, and if I have some kind of existence after I die, then it may not be so radical a change after all. That's how my thinking went. Not bad for an amateur philosopher.

Although I had not previously given much conscious thought to any kind of existence after death, it occurred to me that I did have an opinion about it. If there is nothing after death, if one just went out of existence, why would I feel guilty for not having said *kaddish* for my parents, as though I were depriving them of something? How could I be depriving them of anything if they no longer existed? Why did I feel relieved when Rabbi Segal told me that I could still add to their merits? Obviously, I must believe that their *neshamos* exist.

But my feeling that their *neshamos* exist hardly proves that to be a fact. No jury would accept my feeling as reliable evidence. In order to relieve my anxiety about going out of existence, I had to have more proof.

The session began with Rabbi Segal asking if there were any unresolved questions following the previous session. I asked if he could expound a bit more on the nature of the *neshamah*. Inasmuch as the author of *Path of the Just* says that man's primary obligation on earth is to earn the bliss that the *neshamah* will experience after one dies, then the *neshamah* is really the focal point of life, yet we seem to know so little about it.

Rabbi Segal said that our knowledge of the *neshamah* is rather limited. He referred back to an earlier statement, that when God blew a breath of life into man, He blew something from within Himself into man. Of course, the act of blowing is a physical act, and we cannot ascribe physical acts to God. But the Torah uses words to enable us to have some grasp of things that are beyond our experience. In whatever way God instilled the *neshamah* within man, it is part of Himself. Therefore, just as we cannot have precise knowledge about God's essence, we cannot have precise knowledge of the essence of the *neshamah*.

The Talmud states that the Psalmist repeats the phrase "Let my soul bless God" five times, because the *neshamah* resembles God in five ways. God fills the entire world; the *neshamah* fills the entire body. God sees but cannot be seen; the *neshamah* sees but cannot be seen. God sustains the world; the *neshamah* sustains the body. God is pure; the *neshamah* is pure. God is concealed; the *neshamah* is concealed.

The Talmud concludes, "Let the one who possesses these five characteristics give praise to God Who has these five characteristics." It is the *neshamah* that makes man Godlike and it is the most prominent feature that separates man from other living things.

No one questions that human beings are qualitatively different from animals, Rabbi Segal said. But in what way? Science seems satisfied to designate human beings as *homo sapiens*. "*Sapiens*" means "intellect." Man is, therefore, an intellectual hominoid, or simply a highly intelligent chimpanzee. If people understood the meaning of *homo sapiens*, they would feel highly insulted by this scientific appellation.

Rabbi Segal continued, "There are a number of other ways in which human beings are distinct from animals. First of all, people have free choice as to their actions. Animals do not. An animal must do whatever its body dictates. If it is hungry, it has no choice but to look for food. A human being may set aside his hunger drive, whether in effort to lose weight or for religious considerations, such as fasting on Yom Kippur. A human being is therefore free to choose. He can defy bodily urges because of ethical and moral convictions. An animal cannot.

"People can contemplate a purpose for their existence. Animals cannot. True, a person may not come to any firm conclusions about his purpose in life, but he has the ability to reflect on it, which animals cannot do.

"People have the ability to consciously and volitionally

improve themselves. We can think, 'What must I do to be a better person?' Can you imagine a cow thinking, 'What must I do to be a better cow?'

"You may say, 'How do you know what animals do or do not think?' Well, how do you know that animals are not *sapiens*? Perhaps they have their own equivalent of Mozart or Tolstoy. Just as they do not know about our intellectual achievements, we may not know about theirs. Yet, science assumes that animals are not *sapiens,* and no one seems to question that assumption. Similarly, we may safely conclude that animals lack these other abilities of which we have spoken.

"The sum total of all the traits that are unique to a human being and that distinguish him from animals is what we refer to as the *spirit.*

"Our ethical works describe several levels of the human spirit. There is the *nefesh,* which is the vital force within a person that invigorates him physiologically; there is *ruach,* which literally means 'wind' which is the source of other than physical features, such as thought and intellect; and there is *neshamah,* which is the sacred component within a person, and it is of the *neshamah* that the Torah says that man was created in the likeness of God.

"Although we cannot describe the essence of the *neshamah,* we can know of its existence by its functions. No one has ever seen gravity, yet, because we know that objects thrown up in the air fall to the ground, we know that there must be a gravitational force that causes this to happen. Similarly, we can know something about the *neshamah* from observation of its effects.

"There is universal agreement that everything in the world serves some purpose. Even avowed atheists agree to this. Those who deny creation and believe that the world evolved out of primordial matter, and that all living things are the result of some type of evolutionary process, nevertheless see a kind of 'purpose' in evolution. The classic Darwinian theory of the process of natural selection or the "survival of the fittest" is based on the theory that those creatures survived whose traits served the purpose of existence. Nothing in nature is haphazard or purposeless, because haphazard traits or beings would have fallen by the wayside.

"Once we assume purposefulness in the world, we may ask, what is the purpose of all the traits that are unique to the human being? They can hardly all be in the interest of survival. Clearly, creatures that do not have a superior intellect and that operate totally on instinct have a much better chance of survival. What is the survival value of free choice? Animals instinctively avoid plants that are poisonous for them, whereas human beings, in full awareness that cigarettes cause cancer, emphysema and heart disease, knowingly poison themselves. On a winter day, you may see people standing outside an office building, shivering in the cold, poisoning themselves with nicotine. Man is free to choose self-destruction, which is the antithesis of self-survival.

"History is replete with instances of people who have chosen to die rather than to violate their belief. Whence comes such ultimate self-sacrifice? From the evolutionary process? Hardly. Martyrdom does not contribute to the survival of the species.

"I dare say that many people, even if not highly spiritual, think of self-improvement. A violinist may spend many hours trying to perfect his playing even if he is not a virtuoso who performs public concerts. He is driven by a desire to improve himself. This is true of many artists. This desire does not contribute to survival of the species or even to personal survival.

"The uniquely human traits point to a component within

the human being that is not of a physical nature. This is the *neshamah*.

"While the *neshamah*, which, as we have postulated, is Godly in essence and hence is perfect, it is housed within a physical body which grossly lacks perfection. There is a tug-of-war between the body and the *neshamah*, with the body craving physical gratification and the *neshamah* trying to convert *the whole person* to be Godlike.

"I came across a convincing argument. Suppose you saw a child wearing clothes that were far too large for him. The trousers drag behind him, the sleeves reach the ground, and the hat covers his nose. Obviously, these clothes were not intended for him. The child has put on his father's clothes.

"The human intellect and all the other uniquely human traits are far too large for the mere purpose of sustaining the body for an earthly existence. Man would be much more efficient and a good deal happier if he did not have a powerful mind. It is precisely man's intellect that is the source of his anxiety and agony. It is these products of the intellect that cause people worry and frustration, and which contribute to heart disease and a host of other maladies.

"The uniquely human traits can only be for something beyond physical survival and physical well-being. They can only be for some ultimate goal other than comfort and survival. They point to a supra-physical component of man, which we speak of as the *neshamah*. They attest to the existence of the *neshamah* just as the apple falling to the ground attests to the existence of the law of gravity."

Rabbi Segal pushed his chair back a bit, took a few sips of water, and looked at me with a smile. His unspoken question was, "Does that answer your question about the *neshamah*?" I just loved the man for his warmth as well as his wisdom and sensitivity. I felt safe enough to say, "You certainly have made a convincing case for the *neshamah*, Rabbi. But remember, I am a lawyer. It is not enough for me to make just a convincing argument for a jury. It must be 'beyond a reasonable doubt.' I'm not sure that we're there yet with the *neshamah*."

Rabbi Segal chuckled, as did everyone in the group. "Well stated," he said. "Correct me if I'm wrong, but the standard of 'beyond reasonable doubt' applies only in regard to convicting a person of a crime, which verdict could seriously affect his life. Verdicts regarding money matters do not have to meet the 'beyond reasonable doubt' standard.

"Inasmuch as we are in fact dealing with life-altering concepts, you are justified in requesting even stronger proof for the *neshamah*."

Rabbi Segal then fielded some questions from the group. It was refreshing that he did not claim to have all the answers. "Remember," he said, "that belief in God is a matter of faith, as is the existence of the *neshamah*. By definition, we cannot demonstrate its existence as we do of something in the laboratory. There will always be some element of doubt. But perhaps, as our lawyer friend has said, we may try to bring our belief to 'beyond a *reasonable* doubt.' " And with that, the session was adjourned.

At the next session, Jeff, the psychologist said, "There seems to be pretty convincing evidence from books for the survival of the soul, where information was revealed that could only have come from having had a previous existence. There have also been a large number of 'near-death' experiences, with similar reports of seeing a very bright light and being welcomed by one's departed relatives. That should satisfy the needs of 'beyond a reasonable doubt.'"

Rabbi Segal said, "I must admit that these reports have been intriguing, and for a while I dabbled in para-psychology. But I am by nature a skeptic, and I am not ready to stake my belief on the immortality of the soul on these findings. I am much more impressed by the logical argument of Luzzato, the author of *Path of the Just*.

"We have stipulated the axiom of belief in God and that He created the world. Even a cursory observation of the world and of history reveals the gross lack of justice in the world. Moses himself was bothered by this, and asked God why bad things happen to good people. The Talmud says that God told Moses that as long as he inhabited a physical body, he could not understand this. The explanation would come to him only after he had passed away.

"When we see how many good people suffer while many bad people thrive in comfort, our sense of justice is stressed. If the *only* existence we have is in this world and death is a finality to our existence, we would come to only two conclusions: (1) There is no God and things happen because they happen. Might may be right, as it so often appears to be, or (2) there is a God Who created and operates the world, but He is guilty of malicious mischief. Given the agony to which He subjects some people, He may even be sadistic. With the vast amount of suffering in the world, it is impossible to conceive of an omnipotent God as being benevolent. A belief in God as benevolent is incompatible with a concept of human life coming to a complete end with death.

"Inasmuch as we believe that God is benevolent, we are compelled to conclude that there is much more to one's existence than the sojourn on earth. There is an eternal world where pure justice is carried out. People who suffer in this world are properly compensated in the eternal world.

"One may ask, why does God inflict distress and then compensate for it? Better to not cause suffering, and there will be no need to compensate. There are answers to this question which we will soon discuss.

"The Talmud says that even the most profligate sinner does something which merits being rewarded. God discharges the obligation to reward him by giving him much in this temporal world. On the other hand, even the most righteous person is not completely free of any sin, and God causes him to bear the consequences of his occasional sin in this world, so that he may receive an undiluted reward in the eternal world."

One of the group said, "I don't recall the Torah saying anything about reward in the eternal world."

"You are right," Rabbi Segal said, "and many theologians give explanations for this. Some say that the Torah so greatly emphasizes life that it does not wish to glorify death by speaking of the afterlife. Remember, the generation that received the Torah had emerged from Egypt, a culture where death rather than life was glorified. The pyramids are the tombs of the royalty, and the Egyptian kings were entombed with great riches. The Torah is a program for proper living. Indeed, the Torah considers the dead body to be *tamei*, which means that although it is in itself holy and must be treated with great reverence, it contaminates anyone who comes into contact with it. The Torah diverts us from preoccupation with death.

"Another explanation is that there are simply no words that can do justice to the afterlife. Other religions describe heaven as a place where all of a person's earthly desires and lusts can be gratified. This is offensive to anyone who values spirituality. The prophet, speaking of *Gan Eden* (Paradise) says, 'It cannot be seen by any eye, only by God.' Putting it into the written Torah would concretize it. It was, therefore, relegated to be transmitted orally, which is far less limiting.

"Nevertheless, there are numerous allusions to an afterlife in the Torah. For example, when speaking of the death of a *tzaddik*, the Torah says, 'He was gathered to his people.' That is a rather strange way to refer to death. But what it means is that upon dying, a *tzaddik's neshamah* is not lost, but becomes part of his nation. The Torah also states that God does not postpone reward for the wicked, but gives it to them in this world so that they have no claim to the eternal world.

"We have noted Luzzato's explanation for man's sojourn on earth. But even without that, it is difficult to think of meaning and ultimate purpose to life if it consists only of the few decades on earth and then abruptly fades into oblivion.

"This is what Solomon says in Ecclesiastes: He repeatedly uses the phrase 'under the sun' to refer to earthly existence, and says, 'It is a nothingness of nothingness. There is no gain for all that one does *under the sun*,' meaning that the gain we do have is *above* the sun, celestial, in the supernal, spiritual world.

"As a powerful monarch, Solomon says that he had availed himself of every conceivable earthly pleasure one can imagine, but all that is nothingness. Anyone who has made a deep-seated investment in this world will find Ecclesiastes very depressing, because Solomon totally demolishes worldly accomplishments. Anything we do has significance only because we have an eternal existence."

Rabbi Segal then returned to the text of *Path of the Just*, which discusses the need to avoid sinful behavior and methods used to avoid it. Luzzato certainly had a good understanding of human nature.

On Passover I took the whole family to a kosher resort. It was great having my parents and children together. Marvin asked the Four Questions to his great-grand-father. I prayed that one day, I, too, might hear a great-grandson asking me the Four Questions. But Marvin is just nine. It will be a good twenty years before his child will be able to ask me the Four Questions. Am I not asking too much to live for twenty years? Perhaps I should be content with being at Marvin's Bar-Mitzvah.

The seder at the resort was conducted by a young rabbi, still wet behind the ears, but a very charming young man. We sang the traditional Passover songs. Along the way, as we read the Haggadah, the rabbi would make a few explanatory comments.

Toward the end of the seder, my head was a bit foggy because of the four cups of wine. Everyone joined in singing the *Chad Gadya* ballad, where the cat ate the young kid, was eaten by the dog that was beaten by a stick, etc. It ends with God slaying the Angel of Death. I was not clear-minded enough to grasp everything the rabbi said, but he said that at the end of time, whatever that means, God would slay the Angel of Death and there would be no more death. People would live forever, as was God's intention before Adam and Eve sinned and unleashed death upon the world. The prophet says that God would then wipe away tears from all faces. This would be the era when all humankind would recognize the true God.

I thought, why would God slay the Angel of Death? What had he done to deserve this? He was only carrying out the taks for which he was created. And if there was no more use for him because people would no longer be dying, why slay him? Why not just retire him on a pension? I was going to ask the rabbi to explain this, but I was too groggy. I will pose this question to Rabbi Segal.

The idea that there would be no more death was comforting. It meant that there really was no place for death in God's design of the world, except that it was the consequence of Adam disobeying God. Man was intended to live eternally. I liked that idea.

After the first two days of Passover, I called Rabbi Segal with my question. He agreed that man would have lived very long, if not eternally, had it not been for Adam's sin. But the Divine decree to Adam was, "You were taken from the earth and you will return to the earth." It was only man's *body* that was taken from the earth that would disintegrate and return to dust. But man's soul was not taken from the earth, so its existence was not affected by Adam's sin, and the soul will live eternally.

As far as slaying the Angel of Death, it was not because he took people's lives. That was his job. Rather, it is because the Talmud says that the Angel of Death is Satan, who exceeded his mission in causing man to sin and to turn against God. It is for this reason that the Angel of Death would be destroyed.

Although I had no pretension to live "to the end of time," the thought that one day death would be eliminated was comforting. What was really bothering me was the idea that "Poof! No more Alan Silverman."

Was I the only person who craved some kind of eternal existence? Obviously not. Why do people seek to immortalize themselves by building structures that will bear their names after they are gone? Why do some people choose their monuments? It can only be because they feel this gives them some kind of presence after death. But this is rather foolish. My client, Henry, will no doubt have a huge obelisk on his grave. So what? Nobody will give him much thought by looking at his huge monument. That is hardly a desirable way to continue to exist after death. But come to think of it, Henry did not have too much of a presence even when he was alive. People whose lives are more spiritual than Henry's should have a spiritual existence after they die. That seems only fair, and is a reasonable argument for the ongoing existence of the soul.

The resort provided entertainment every night of the Passover week. There was a band, a comedian, and a magician who did fascinating tricks. I enjoyed watching Marvin watching the magician more than I enjoyed the magic.

The resort also had a nutritionist who gave a lecture on proper diet. My Adina was in her glory. She, of course, insisted that every family member attend. She had given up the fight to cure my disease with tons of grapes or grapefruit, I forget which.

I thought it was actually funny, having a lecture on proper diet while we were wolfing down *knaidlach* (dumplings), deep fried potato *latkes,* and a variation of potato preparations, in addition to matzah.

One day, the resort had a psychologist who led a "sensitivity group." I had nothing better to do, so I attended. There were about twenty people in the group. He began by asking us to identify ourselves and say a few words about ourselves. When my turn came, I gave my name, my residence, and that I was a lawyer and married with two grown children. That was pretty much the way everyone identified themselves.

The psychologist said, "I asked you to say a few words about yourself, and all of you did, yet I know very little about you other than your name, where you live, how many are in your family, and what you do for a living. I know that you are an accountant, you are a housewife, you are an insurance agent, you are a lawyer, you are a dentist, and so on for all of you. You have told us what you *do*, but not what you *are*. How about if we tried it again, but this time tell us something about who you *are*?"

The circle began with the woman sitting next to me. She was caught off guard and was grasping for something to say. "Well," she said, "as I said, I am a social worker. I work for a Jewish Family Service. I was past president of Hadassah. What else can I tell you? I have a lovely granddaughter, six months old, and I love to babysit for her."

I identified with this woman's frustration. What was I going to say about myself? That I built up the largest Jewish law firm in the city? That's just more of what I did. I didn't really understand what the psychologist meant by what we *are*.

Fortunately, I didn't have to follow the woman. The psychologist said, "O.K., now you've told us a little about who you are. You are a person who is interested in helping others outside of your job, which is why you donated your time to Hadassah. You are a person who loves children, because clearly your six-month-old granddaughter sometimes cries and needs to be carried and cuddled.

"All of us have personality traits that constitute who we *are*. We may be empathic and desirous of strong friendship. We may be introverted and prefer to be alone. We may have a desire to help others, or we may believe that everyone should carry their own weight. We may like music or drama, needlepoint or painting. We may love nature and the out-of-doors, or prefer the concrete buildings of a busy city. We may love flowers, putter in the garden, perhaps have a little patch where we grow some vegetables. We may love fishing or golf. We may like to take our children or grandchildren to a ball game. We may be religious, attending services regularly, or we may just attend on the High Holidays. We may be tolerant and patient, or bigoted and short-fused. There are virtually endless ways in which we can describe ourselves.

"What I wish to point out is that most people don't think of their identity in those terms, but rather in externals. Their names, where they live, and their occupation.

"This reminds me of a story," the psychologist said. "A man was having difficulty finding his clothes when he woke up in the morning, so he decided to make a list of where all his things were before he retired. He awoke in the morning and read his list. 'Here is my underwear, here is my socks, here is my shirt, here is my necktie, here are my trousers, here are my shoes, here is my jacket, and here is my hat.' Then he paused a minute and said, 'But where am I?'

"Sometimes we don't get around to thinking about who we really are until we realize that we are *not* the external appearance that we present to the world," the psychologist said.

Fortunately, I was not called upon next. Another woman was intrigued by this idea and raised her hand to be recognized. She began telling something about herself. Just then my cellular phone rang. It was my office. I excused myself from the group to take the call.

I felt relieved that I did not have to talk about myself. Then it occurred to me. What had extricated me? The office. That was my real identity. I was Alan Silverman, the managing partner of a law firm. Was there a real "me" that I did not know?

I recalled how Evelyn would ask me to refrain from calling the office when we were on vacation. Why did I feel compelled to do so? Why couldn't I just relax? Was it, perhaps, because unless I was functioning as a lawyer I was uneasy because I had no other identity?

I though a good bit about this, and I decided that I would have to acquire an identity other than my profession. I should be a *person* who is a lawyer rather than *being* nothing else other than a lawyer.

My introspection did not last very long. As soon as we returned home, I jumped back into work with both feet. A few weeks later we won a big case with a seven figure fee. We brought out the champagne and celebrated.

I was approaching one year since my condition had been diagnosed, and I was feeling good. In fact, I had gone back to driving through the tunnel, and it did not bother me. I was one of the cases that had been cured.

One day Evelyn received a call that her father had suffered a stroke. She immediately left to be with her mother. Evelyn has a younger sister who was divorced and was caring for two adolescents, one of whom was a "special needs" child. Her sister could not leave them, so Evelyn was the one to go.

Hadassah had her own apartment, and she offered to stay with me while Evelyn was gone. I thanked her but told her that I did to need to be baby-sat.

The moment of truth occurred when I returned home from the office the day that Evelyn left. I was alone in this huge house. This was not the first time Evelyn was away, but it was very different. In the past I had been invincible, but now I was vulnerable. My feeling of being Superman had been shattered. My having been "cured" of a malignant disease was as illusory as the slight-of-hand tricks of the magician at the resort.

I felt very insecure, even threatened. I realized how dependent I had become on Evelyn and I was ashamed of my neediness.

I tried to distract myself by watching TV, but it was to no avail. I was anxious and did not know what to do about it. Perhaps I should call Dr. Berman and ask him to prescribe a tranquilizer. I would never get to sleep in this condition.

The phone rang. It was Hadassah, wanting to know if I was OK. "I'm fine," I lied. I was not about to admit my frailty to anyone else.

"I'm not comfortable with you being alone, Daddy," Hadassah said. "I'm going to come over until Mom comes back."

"Good girl," I thought. "Well," I said, "if it's going to make you feel better, OK." I thought, "Thank God."

With Hadassah in the house, my introspection returned. My attitude of invulnerability all these years was a sham. I was still the frightened little boy who cried when he fell off the bike. Part of me had never grown up. I was probably always needy, but in impressing everyone else with my power, I had succeeded in denying my neediness to myself. It had never surfaced until now, when the threat of my illness and Evelyn's absence coalesced to break through my denial.

I thought about the times that I had lost control of my anger and screamed at Evelyn. I could not remember the specific instances, but perhaps those were times when something she had said touched a raw nerve in my fragile ego. After all, I was a lawyer to everyone else, and that is where my strength lay.

But I wasn't a lawyer to Evelyn. I didn't have that defensive armor in relating to her. If anyone was critical of me as a lawyer, I could easily defend myself. But to Evelyn I was just her husband, a person. Sure, Evelyn respected me for my achievements, but that was not the essence of my relationship with her. So I was vulnerable.

I recalled having thrown a few tantrums as a child. Which child doesn't? And what were my anger outbursts at Evelyn other than the reaction of that part of me that had never grown up, the scared child inside of me?

So who is the real me? Rabbi Segal said that it is not the body, but the *neshamah*. What do I know of the *neshamah*? Next to nothing. Rabbi Segal said that healing of the spirit precedes healing of the body. Can I get well without doing something more to improve my spirit?

Since childhood, I had grown physically. My body was that of an adult. But what about my spirit? Had I tended to it and nurtured it so that it, too, could grow? Is it possible that the child within me, that part of me that is so needy and insecure, is the spiritual part of me that had not matured along with my body and mind? The psychologist in our study group seems to be very bright. Perhaps I should have a few sessions with him, or maybe I should first speak a bit more with Rabbi Segal. I would have to think about it.

E velyn called me three times a day. Her father's condition had stabilized. It was considered a "mild" stroke. It had affected his right side and his speech, but he did have some function in his arm and leg and could make himself understood. He was going to be transferred to a rehabilitation center for therapy and would be home in a few weeks. Evelyn would stay until after the transfer. In the meantime, Adina and Hadassah were looking after their father, and I appreciated every bit of it.

I had another pre-session discussion with Rabbi Segal and told him about my identity concerns. I asked if I should see a psychologist to deal with my unresolved childhood issues. He felt that a psychologist would be helpful, but he did not feel that a visit would resolve my identity problems.

I don't think Rabbi Segal had any formal training in psychology, but he is extremely intuitive. He agreed that my preoccupation with my profession had been a defense against my feelings of inadequacy as a person, and he felt that spiritual development would give me a better sense of self.

He said that this issue was of importance to everyone and that he would bring it up at the study group.

Rabbi Segal began the session by focusing on the theme of the first chapter of *Path of the Just*: man's obligation on earth. He said that it was not crucial that we accept Luzzato's opinion about our purpose in the world. What *is* crucial is that we have *some* concept of an ultimate purpose. Without that, Rabbi Segal said, we cannot be truly happy.

"To be happy, a person must have a sense of self-worth. Without a feeling of self-worth a person will feel so unhappy that he will go to any lengths to feel good. One person may resort to alcohol to take away his feelings of discontent. Another may become a food addict or a compulsive gambler. Yet another may become a workaholic. Another person may pursue fame or public recognition.

"Many people go through life without giving much thought, if any, to an ultimate purpose, but their ignoring it does not take away from its importance. If they feel discontented and are not aware of the true reason for their unhappiness, they are likely to look for things to blame it on. One person may blame his job, another her husband or his wife, another the community he lives in. In desperation to feel better, people may change jobs, divorce, or move to another city. Of course, none of these maneuvers address the basic issue. It is particularly tragic when a marriage breaks up for such reasons, because it impacts negatively on both partners, who remain unhappy, and on the children. If the true reason for the discontent is not addressed, a second marriage will not be any happier in the long run than the first."

Rabbi Segal paused, as if to give us some time to absorb what he had said. He looked around the group for comments. When no one said anything, he continued.

"How does one achieve a sense of self-worth? Well, how do we assign value to anything? If we look at all our possessions, we will find that there are essentially two criteria that determine value: function and esthetics. The picture on the wall may have no function, but it is decorative. Things that are not of esthetic value are valued for their function.

"Suppose you have a beautiful antique grandfather clock whose mechanism breaks down. Although it no longer tells time, you keep it because it is an attractive piece of furniture. But what happens when your can-opener becomes dull and won't open cans? You relegate it to the trash bucket. It is of no esthetic value. You can hardly display it as you would a fine piece of crystal or china.

"If we apply these criteria to ourselves, what do we find? True, some people are so handsome that they may consider themselves ornamental. That does not apply to most of us, and even those who have been blessed with beautiful features must realize that with aging, this esthetic value will decrease. What we are left with, then, is our function.

"We all do something for a livelihood, but it is difficult to assume that my purpose on earth is to paint houses, repair umbrellas, or even remove appendixes. These provide for an income, but do not provide a sense of fulfillment of an ultimate goal.

"One may say that helping other people is an ultimate goal. That is indeed commendable, and I wish that more people would feel that way. But even that is not completely satisfying.

"A bright little girl asked her mother, 'Mommy, what are we here for?' The mother, imbued with humanitarian ideals said, 'We're here to help other people, honey.' The little girl was satisfied and went out to play, only to return a bit later, asking, 'And what are the other people here for?'

"As noble a cause as helping other people is, it does not satisfy the need for an ultimate purpose.

"If the existence of the universe is a haphazard accident

and has no ultimate purpose, it is rather meaningless to seek a purpose in a purposeless world. If we take the leap of faith and believe that there is a God, a Higher Intelligence Who brought the universe into being for a purpose known only to Him, we can then speak sensibly about a purpose in existence.''

"The noble act of helping others because it is a mitzvah, because God instructed us to do so, now becomes purposeful. This is equally true of respecting one's parents, giving *tzedakah*, avoiding gossip, and being truthful. These commendable behaviors take on a different significance because they contribute to the purpose for which God created human life.''

Again Rabbi Segal paused. It gave me a moment to reflect on the celebration in the office when our case concluded with triumph. The fee was indeed significant, and the multinational corporation we represented won its right to retain exclusive production of its product. A fine achievement. But could I see this as the purpose of my existence? Hardly, anymore than I could see extricating my client, Henry, from the thorny legal problems in building his empire.

One of the group said, "I'm not sure I understand your point. Helping others or respecting one's parents is the same act whether a person does so because he understands it to be right and proper or because he believes it is a mitzvah. In what way are the two different?'

Rabbi Segal responded, "Right and proper? The unaided human intellect is unreliable to decide what is right and proper. That is why the Torah says, 'You shall do what is right and proper in the eyes of God.'

"History has demonstrated the fallibility of human intellect in determining what is morally and ethically correct. Some pagan rituals were grossly obscene, and infanticide and human sacrifice were considered laudable. That can happen when man fashions his own religion.

"But we do not have to go back to ancient history to see that the unaided human intellect is unreliable. The horrors of the Holocaust were committed by the nation that was foremost in academic and intellectual excellence.

"The Holocaust actually began with the social sanction of eliminating people who were born with such gross defects that they could never make any contribution to society. Not only were they a drain on society and a source of great misery to their parents, but many of them led a life of suffering. It was seen as an act of mercy to them, their parents, and society to eliminate them. This was rather an easy sell, and once this was accepted, it was only a small progression to eliminate all the undesirables, which, of course, were the Jews. The Final Solution was fashioned by some of the most advanced intellects in the world.

"But we needn't even go back to Nazi Germany to see how treacherous the unaided human intellect can be. Ever since America was founded, euthanasia had been considered morally wrong, just another form of murder. We now have several states which have legalized euthanasia. How did this come about? Purely because we have become more sensitive to human suffering? Hardly. It is rather obvious that the country is threatened by the collapse of the social security system because medical advances have prolonged the lives of people far beyond their productive years.

"Because it has been demonstrated that the lion's share of Medicare expenditures are incurred in the last six months of people's lives, the state of Oregon has curtailed paying for certain treatments to people over age eighty. This is a harbinger, foretelling the course of the future.

"God's word is eternal and immutable. Human life never loses its value. The elderly person or the child born with serious birth defects have the same claim to life as the greatest scientist. Healing the sick is not merely an obligation imposed by society. It is a mitzvah, and is regulated by the laws of mitzvah rather than by legislatures and courts."

One of the group asked, "But how can anyone be certain of what his function or purpose is?"

Rabbi Segal said, "There may not be any logical certainty, and that is why we speak of a 'leap of faith.' But even certainty is not crucial. What is important is that we reflect upon this. I dare say that most people don't give this much thought at all. Luzzato and the other theologians say that it is the work of the *yetzer hara*, the evil inclination within us, to distract us from such considerations. We become so absorbed in our work and in a myriad of pastimes that we do not pay attention to ideas of ultimate goal and purpose.

"Furthermore, we may be deterred from looking for an ultimate goal and purpose by the fact that awareness of an ultimate goal and purpose may impinge on some of the gratification and pleasures we enjoy. The philosophy of 'Eat, drink, and be merry for tomorrow we die,' allows one to strive for maximum pleasure. If there is nothing else to live for, why should one not seek to attain maximum pleasure? However, if there is an ultimate goal, that may require sacrificing some pleasures. When one has a goal of becoming a doctor or a lawyer, one must spend many hours in study, time which could otherwise be spent having fun. But one must eschew much fun in order to achieve the goal of becoming accredited in those professions. Similarly, living with a specific goal in mind may call for eschewing some pleasurable activities.

"Our judgment capacity is vulnerable to being bribed. Because we are desirous of pleasures, our thinking may be distorted so that we conclude that what we want is the right and proper thing. We cannot be objective in our judgment. The *yetzer hara* exploits this vulnerability to divert us away from thinking of ultimate goal and purpose, because the latter may call for denying ourselves some of the pleasures of life.

"As intelligent people, we should be aware of our vulnerability, and struggle against our natural inclinations for pleasure to reflect upon finding an ultimate goal and purpose in life."

We all looked at each other. I don't know about the others in the group, but with me, Rabbi Segal had hit the bull's-eye. I realized that I hadn't been satisfied with me, and that I had covered up my dissatisfaction with my striving for professional excellence. I had to do some reflecting as to what I was supposed to do with my life.

Evelyn came home, and I lost no time in telling her how much I had missed her. I also did something I had never done before. I apologized to her for the times I had lost control and had been nasty to her.

I had always thought apologizing to be demeaning. Admission of having been wrong was a sign of weakness. But after I apologized to Evelyn, I felt much better about myself. Apologizing is not at all demeaning. To the contrary, it is edifying.

It was still two months to Rosh Hashanah. By that time Evelyn's father would be home. I told Evelyn we could make whatever necessary accommodations for her parents to be here again this year. She was very appreciative of that.

I brought Evelyn up to date on what had transpired at the office, and I said, "You were right, honey. There'll be no more calling the office when we're on vacation. I've come to realize that my whole existence was as a lawyer, and that if I wasn't functioning as a lawyer, I was nothing. That is changing. I'm beginning to think of myself primarily as a person who happens to be a lawyer. I don't think I can make a radical change overnight, but I'm heading in that direction."

Evelyn became teary eyed. "I love you," she said.

"I think this has something to do with my increasing awareness of my mortality. It's too bad that it took a disease to shake me into reality. I don't want to go out of existence. I can't have an eternal existence as a lawyer. Sure, the name Silverman and Rabin can remain on the fourteenth floor of the Arrow Building forever, but that's not me. I don't know in what way I can assure my existence, but it is certainly not as a lawyer."

Evelyn smiled. "If that's what those sessions with the group at Rabbi Segal's is accomplishing, I'm going to go back with you."

"My body is not forever and my profession is not forever," I said. "Rabbi Segal says it's my *neshamah,* and he thinks I have a beautiful *neshamah.* I'm willing to keep an open mind."

That night I had a dream. I often dream, but hardly ever remember them. This one I remembered after I awoke. I was in a strange city that I could not recognize. I was looking for my car, but could not remember in which of the many parking lots I had parked it. I felt anxious, because I couldn't go around to every parking lot in the city. There was some other stuff that I could not remember. Then I saw my Zeide, who was smiling and said, "You left your car near the succah." I awoke laughing.

At breakfast, I told Evelyn about the dream. She said, "You don't have to be Freud to interpret that dream. What you were looking for was yourself, but you had no idea where you would find yourself. Your grandfather said that you would find yourself near the succah, whatever that means."

"I'm not sure what that means," I said, "but we'll put up a succah this year, and Marvin will help me decorate it."

I hadn't thought that Evelyn was serious about coming to the study group, but she in fact did.

It was my father's *yahrzeit*, and I made my regular visit to the cemetery, only this time there was a difference. Two rows up were the plots I had acquired for myself and Evelyn. To my own amazement, it did not upset me.

At the next group session I asked Rabbi Segal why we light a candle on the *yahrzeit* of a parent. He quoted a verse from Proverbs, "A lamp of God is man's soul, probing all its chambers." Kindling a light is symbolic of our awareness that a person's *neshamah* is a lamp of God. Rabbi Segal arose and took a book from the shelf. "Listen to what Rabbi Samson Raphael Hirsch says: 'The very soul you harbor within you proclaims God's seeing and hearing. Can you not feel that, with this soul, God has implanted His lamp within you, that it fills every crevice of your inner being with its light, and that it listens to you? Can you not sense that it censures all your mistakes, warns you before you commit a wrong, gives you no peace after you have done it, and does not let you enjoy life until you have admitted your wrong before God and promised atonement and betterment? This Divine light, which we call conscience, is also a seeing of God's eyes and a hearing of God's ear."

Wow! I had asked a simple question and got a fire and brimstone sermon in response.

"The light we kindle on the day we commemorate the death of a parent, who now exists as a pure *neshamah,* is to stimulate us to a soul-searching," Rabbi Segal said. "We need not grope in the dark. The *neshamah* is a lamp which provides light so that we can see which path to follow and avoid the pitfalls along the way.

"Soul-searching is generally thought to mean doing a kind of moral inventory, searching within oneself. Another way of looking at soul-searching is searching *for* the soul, searching to find oneself. The *neshamah* is a Divine light which can help us find ourselves, who we *really* are instead of who we *think* we are."

Searching for oneself! Wasn't that what I was doing in the dream, looking for where I'd parked my car? And Zeide said it was near the succah, the succah which Rabbi Segal said represented our temporary existence on earth, but which is celebrated as a joyous rather than solemn holiday, because during this sojourn on earth we have the opportunity to prepare for an eternal existence. And the author of *Path of the Just* said that this is what our primary function on earth is, to prepare ourselves for the eternal existence. It was all beginning to fit together.

At one study session, Jeff the psychologist said, "I'd like some clarification. When I mentioned the report of people going back to previous existences under hypnosis, you dismissed these, saying you were skeptical. But doesn't Judaism believe in reincarnation?"

Rabbi Segal said, "There is a strong basis for reincarnation. It is not the same as resurrection of the dead, which Maimonides lists as one of the thirteen tenets of faith that we *must* accept.

"I don't know much about reincarnation, although I assume it to be true. My skepticism about what you are describing is that I do not feel that previous existences can be discovered by hypnosis."

One of the group quipped, "I think reincarnation is a great idea. I'd just like to know who I'm going to be in my next existence so that I could will all my money to him." We all laughed.

Rabbi Segal said, "The concept of reincarnation is a kabbalistic one. It was popularized by Rabbi Yitzchak Luria, a fifteenth century Torah scholar, who is generally referred to by the eponym 'the Ari.' Although he did not write any books himself, his disciples recorded his teachings. One of their books is 'The Book of Reincarnation,' probably written by his chief disciple, Rabbi Chaim Vital.

"I don't feel competent to discuss reincarnation. However, there is a very fine chassidic rabbi, Rabbi Rabinowitz, who is a Torah scholar and I am certain that he is well versed in the kaballah. If you wish to pursue the subject, you may contact him."

"What is the kaballah?" someone asked.

"The kabbalah is a body of knowledge, often referred to as 'mystic.' A better term would be 'esoteric.' The Talmud deals with a broad range of laws of conduct based on the Torah, practical laws that relate to ritual, marriage, and business, as well as to ethics. The Talmud is clarified by a number of commentaries and is open to all. The kaballah, on the other hand, deals much more with heavenly matters and the principles according to which God governs the world. Much of kabbalah is based primarily on a book called the *Zohar*, which means "light," that is ascribed to R' Shimon bar Yochai, a sage of the Mishnah.

"The word 'kabbalah' means 'received,' and this indicates that it was transmitted from teacher to student, who 're-ceived' its content. This is in contrast to the Talmud, which is an open book which one can study on his own.

"As a youngster, I was fascinated by the kabbalah, but I was discouraged from studying it. First, there was no one I knew who could teach it to me. Learning kabbalah on one's own can be dangerous, because without an instructor one can be misled by erroneous distortions. It is said that the false Messiah of the seventeenth century, Shabbatai Zevi, who caused indescribable harm to the Jews of Eastern Europe, had dabbled in kabbalah and developed the delusion that he was the Messiah. Second, I was told that a prerequisite to studying kabbalah is a thorough knowledge of the Talmud. And finally, it was generally accepted that one must be very mature in order to study kabbalah, so one should not study it until age forty. Although I have met the age criterium, I have not as yet studied the kabbalah.

"I am amused when I see the large number of books written about the kabbalah. People who dabble in these books usually do not meet any of the three prerequisites."

I asked, "And what about the Talmud?"

"The Talmud is open to all. We have classes on the Talmud every evening and on Sunday mornings in the synagogue. You are most welcome to attend."

"I'll do just that," I said to myself.

After the session, Jeff the psychologist and I decided that we would meet with Rabbi Rabinowitz to learn something more about reincarnation.

On Sunday morning, following services, I sat in on
Rabbi Segal's Talmud class. It was an eye opener. I
had no idea what Talmud was all about. The subject
under discussion involved a dispute between two
neighbors. One wished to put a window in a wall that
overlooked his neighbor's yard. The owner of the house said
that he has a right to do anything he wishes with his house.
The neighbor argued that the existing conditions were such
that he had the privacy of his own yard, and that putting a
window in that wall would impinge on his privacy. The
authors of the Talmud engaged in a lively discussion.

Another case. A person wished to erect a wall to enclose his
yard for privacy. The neighbor objected, because the wall
would block the light to his window. Again, a lively discussion.

I was dumbfounded. These are complex issues dealt with in
law school. Laws of privacy did not even come into common
law until the last century, yet the Talmud discussed them two
thousand years ago! I was even more amazed to find out that

these subjects are studied in yeshivah by kids aged twelve! Why, even graduate school law students have to struggle with these concepts. The Sunday morning Talmud class was going to become a staple for me.

I had no aspirations for the mysticism of kabbalah, but I was curious about reincarnation. Jeff, my psychologist friend and I went to see Rabbi Rabinowitz.

Rabbi Rabinowitz had an impressive appearance: a long, gray beard, long side curls called *peyos*, a long satin *kaftan*. He greeted us warmly, with a soft-spoken voice. We told him that we were in Rabbi Segal's study group, discussing *Path of the Just*, and because the author placed so much emphasis on the existence after death, we were interested in finding out more about reincarnation.

Rabbi Rabinowitz said, "Ah, *Path of the Just*. What a marvelous book! I'm so glad you mentioned it. I made a resolution to follow the author's instructions and reread the book periodically. It just dawned on me that it has been several months since my last reading of it, and it is time that I review it once again. You know, the great Gaon of Vilna, a stellar Torah luminary, would review Chapter Two of *Path of the Just* numerous times before he left his study for the outside world. He was so concerned that exposure to the world outside might distract him from his communion with God, and he felt that *Path of the Just* would protect him from such distraction.

"Yes, Luzzato does emphasize that our earthly existence is to enable us to prepare ourselves for existence in the eternal world. Knowing that there is an existence after death is important because it can determine how we live.

"The Lubavitcher Rebbe kept his yeshivah open in Communist Russia even though he had been repeatedly ordered to disband it. One day a Russian officer entered his study and demanded that he close the yeshivah at once. The Rebbe said,

'I will be loyal to the government and do whatever they ask of me, but this is the one thing I cannot do.'

"The officer pulled out his pistol and said, 'Perhaps this will change your mind.'

"The Rebbe remained unperturbed, with no show of anxiety. 'Your little toy does not frighten me,' he said. 'Someone who has no God or who has a multiplicity of gods but only one world is afraid of dying. I have one God and two worlds, and it is immaterial to me whether I am with Him in this world or the next.' The officer returned his pistol to its holster and departed.

"But just what is the eternal world? What is *Gan Eden* or Paradise — that we cannot know. It is as unknowable as the fourth dimension. The prophet Isaiah says of *Gan Eden* that only God knows what it is. Even the prophets could not envision it.

"We can only know what it is not. It is not, as some people with vulgar thoughts imagine, a place where one can indulge in all physical pleasures. After all, many of the earthly pleasures a human being experiences are no different than those experienced by animals. Far be it to think that the reward of a person who has led a spiritual life will be to indulge in animalistic pleasures.

"*Gan Eden* is a place where our *neshamos* can experience the ultimate spiritual delight of the radiance of God's glory.

"What do we know about reincarnation? This concept was popularized by the Ari, and the rationale is this:

"The *neshamah* was instilled in man by God when He figuratively 'blew' a breath of life into Adam. The *Zohar* says that one who exhales breathes out something from within himself. The *neshamah* which God 'breathed' into man is thus 'part' of God. Of course, God is absolute unity, and there cannot be a 'part' of God. But it is a figure of speech, as if God had spun off something of Himself and placed it within man.

"The *neshamah* is sent down to earth, as Luzzato says, to do the will of God, which will then enable it to return to its source in God. The *neshamah* pines for this reunion, but it cannot achieve this until it has fulfilled the will of God, which is to do the six hundred thirteen mitzvos prescribed in the Torah.

"But it is quite impossible for a person to fulfill all six hundred thirteen mitzvos in a single lifetime. Some mitzvos apply to circumstances to which a person may not relate. For example, there is a mitzvah to redeem a firstborn son from a *kohen*. If one's first child is a girl, he cannot fulfill that mitzvah. It is a mitzvah for a *kohen* to give the priestly blessing. If one is not born a *kohen*, one can never fulfill that mitzvah. And there are many other mitzvos which a person may be unable to fulfill.

"Yet, for the *neshamah* to reunite with God, fulfillment of *all* the mitzvos is necessary. Therefore, the *neshamah* of a person whose first child was a girl is given a second existence where his first child is a boy. Or, one who was an Israelite is given a second existence as a *kohen*, and so it is with other mitzvos. If the six hundred thirteen mitzvos are not completed in the second existence, the *neshamah* comes down in yet another existence.

"Similarly, if one has committed a sin for which he did not atone, his *neshamah* is given the opportunity in another existence to rectify that deficiency. The Ari states that when God told Noah that He was going to destroy the entire population of the world, but that he — Noah and his family — would be saved, Noah, although he was a very righteous man, did not intercede on behalf of his generation. This was a fault that had to be rectified. Noah's *neshamah*, therefore, came down to earth in the person of Moses. When the Israelites sinned with the Golden Calf, God said to Moses, 'I will destroy them and build you into a great nation.' Moses promptly interceded and said, 'If You do not forgive them, erase me as well.' By attaining forgiveness for his generation, Moses rectified Noah's shortcoming.

"A frequently asked question is, 'If a *neshamah* comes down to earth several times and inhabits different bodies, which body does it go to at resurrection?' The answer is that the *neshamah* is not an article which can be in only one place. The *neshamah* is part of God, and just as God is in all places at once, the *neshamah* can also be in several bodies at the same time.

"In the Book of Reincarnation, the Ari reveals the identities of *neshamos* that came down in subsequent existences."

We were quite fascinated by this information. I asked, "What about a *neshamah* being reincarnated in other than in a person, like in an animal?"

Rabbi Rabinowitz said, "I have heard stories like that, but I cannot vouch for their authenticity. I must admit, however, that there are some that I, personally, believe to be true. These can be quite spooky."

"I'm game," I said.

Rabbi Rabinowitz said, "My grandfather told me about a story that happened in his *shtetl*. They did not have kosher supermarkets as we have today. The local butcher would buy a cow, and the *shochet* would slaughter it. The viscera then had to be examined, and if a lesion were found, the rabbi would have to decide whether the animal was kosher or *treife* (not kosher). If it was *treife*, the butcher sustained a loss, because he would have to sell the meat at a lower price to a non-Jewish butcher.

"The local *shochet* told my grandfather this story:

'We regularly did the ritual slaughter on Thursdays, so that the meat would be fresh for Shabbos, because we had no refrigeration. One Monday night I had a dream, in which I heard a message, "I am a *neshamah* anxious to return to *Gan Eden*. However, I was guilty of a sin which I must rectify. The

Heavenly Tribunal wished to send me down to earth again, but I pleaded that my sin was rather minor, and asked if they could find some way to admit me to *Gan Eden* without another sojourn on earth.

"The Tribunal decided that I would be sent to earth as a cow, and that if I were slaughtered ritually, and Jews recited a *berachah* when they ate the meat and used the energy provided by eating the meat to perform mitzvos, that would compensate for my sin and I would be spared another sojourn on earth.

"Tomorrow they will bring me to you for ritual slaughtering. Please be careful that you do the slaughtering properly. If I become *treife*, I will have to come down to earth for another lifetime ordeal, and I shall never forgive you. You will know that this is for real, because I will not allow any *shochet* other than you to slaughter me."

'I awoke in a panic. Then I realized that it was nothing other than a silly dream. Tomorrow is Tuesday, and we never do the slaughtering on Tuesday.

'At the morning service, the butcher came into the *shul*. He was able to buy a cow at a very low price, and wanted it to be slaughtered today. "But we don't slaughter until Thursday," I said. However, the butcher insisted that I do it today. I broke out in a cold sweat. The dream was valid, after all.

'I asked another *shochet* to join me, and I suggested that he do the slaughtering. No sooner did he approach the animal than it began trashing about so vigorously that it was impossible to do the slaughtering. I then approached it, and it was perfectly still. I did the slaughtering perfectly.

'When we inspected the lungs, I almost fainted from shock. There was a lesion on the lung which was generally ruled *treife*. When I showed the lung to the rabbi, he indeed ruled that it was *treife*. I drew upon all my resources of knowledge of the various halachic authorities that considered this lesion kosher, and I was finally able to persuade the rabbi to accept their opinion.

'A similar incident occurred to another *shochet*, who allowed the *treife* ruling to apply. He suddenly lost his sight and was blind for the rest of his life. He had not done his utmost to bring the *neshamah* to its eternal peace.' "

Rabbi Rabinowitz said, "There's a story for you. Of course, you need not believe it. It could be spun out of whole cloth. However, my grandfather was reliably honest, and he knew this *shochet* to be impeccably honest."

Jeff and I sat there in silence. I did not know what to say. Rabbi Rabinowitz was a very mature, sincere person. I did not think of him as being credulous, yet this did not overcome my skepticism. All I could say was, "Wow!" The rabbi saw that I was uncomfortable in reacting, so he just changed the subject.

"Tell me," Rabbi Rabinowitz said, "why are you so curious about reincarnation? What difference does it make to you, or is it just a matter of interest?"

At this point I did not feel comfortable telling the rabbi about my illness, and certainly did not want Jeff to know. I said, "When the subject came up at Rabbi Segal's study group, it whetted my curiosity. For some time I had been thinking about whether we just fade into oblivion when we die, or if there is some kind of existence after death. I Recently had *yahrzeit* for my father, and I wondered if this was just some ceremony of tribute out of respect to him, or something really substantial. For that matter, what is the point of tribute to someone who has died? It can't make any difference to them if they no longer exist. If they cannot appreciate the tribute, why do it? And so I wondered whether reincarnation is the way a person is perpetuated and exists after death."

Rabbi Rabinowitz said, "Whether reincarnation is or is not, the immortality of the *neshamah* is an essential tenet in Judaism. We do believe there is *Gan Eden,* and we believe there is Gehinnom where a *neshamah* may undergo a purification, as it were, to enable its reunification with God. "

We got up to leave. "Give my best to Rabbi Segal," Rabbi Rabinowitz said, "and feel free to come back any time."

On the way out I asked Jeff, "Well, what do you think?"

He responded, "Reincarnation? I don't know. An immortal existence of some kind, yes."

"That's how I feel, too," I said. What I did not tell him was that I felt a sense of relief in knowing that I won't just go out of existence when I die.

Rosh Hashanah came and went. The prayers were much more meaningful to me. I was grateful that I had been inscribed in the Book of Life for another year, and prayed for another wonderful year. My tests had shown that the disease was under control.

Evelyn's parents did come for Rosh Hashanah, and the family gathering was most enjoyable. We wheeled my father-in-law to *shul*. In spite of his disability, his mood was pleasant, almost upbeat. His mental acuity had not been affected. His speech was broken, but we were patient with him until he could make himself understood.

My father-in-law was now eighty-one. Was he productive to society? Not in the usual sense. He was productive to us because we loved him. Parents never outgrow their usefulness. As long as one has a living parent, one can be a child. Most of us wish to hang on to the feeling of being a child. Childhood was so delightful. So much fun, so few responsibilities. What a shame to give it up. Our conscious mind matures and adapts to reality. Our subconscious can ignore reality. We can still be children even when we are grandparents.

I thought, "How terrible that a state government can put an age limit on medical treatments. If an eighty-one year old stroke victim in Oregon required an expensive life-saving procedure, he might not be able to get it. What right did any legislature have to say that my father-in-law's life was not worth saving? Who gave the legislature the right to play God and decide who shall live and who shall die?"

I invited my in-laws to remain with us for a few weeks until after Succos, but my father-in-law made it clear that he wanted to go home. He was obviously more comfortable in the familiar surroundings where he had lived for the past thirty years.

I had ordered a succah. My Zeide used to build his succah out of paneling and old doors. There were no pre-fab succahs in his day. My succah required little construction. It consisted of a brightly colored canvas on a metal frame. The roof covering was of a mat of reeds instead of branches. I was nostalgic about the green branches that covered Zeide's succah.

Marvin came to help decorate the succah. We put up the lights. I had bought some very colorful streamers. Zeide didn't have these; he bought colored crepe paper and cut it into strips to fashion streamers. Zeide, however, would write verses from the Torah and place them on the succah wall, which, of course, I was unable to do.

I did want to recapture a memory. I bought some gold colored spray paint and had Marvin spray several apples gold, which we hung from the succah roof. It wasn't exactly the same, because there was no spray paint in those days. I would paint the apples with the brush that Zeide had used to write the verses.

It was a chilly October night, but who cared? Marvin and I were having too much fun to care about the weather.

Watching Marvin gave me a *déjà vu,* and I had the pleasant thought that perhaps Marvin will one day decorate his succah together with his grandson.

Do you believe in coincidence? I was just about to tell Marvin how Bubby had given me some hot chocolate to dispel the cold of the succah, when Evelyn called out, "How about the two of you coming in for some hot chocolate? You must be freezing out there." I was in disbelief. I said to Evelyn, "What made you say that?" She said, "Why, is there anything wrong with hot chocolate?" "No," I said, "nothing at all. Nothing at all."

I sipped the hot chocolate slowly. I loved the feeling of being a child once again.

Succos was very enjoyable. The first night, Adina, Jack, Marvin, and Hadassah were with us. I don't recall ever having had so wonderful a family meal. We bundled up warmly because the temperature was in the mid-forties. The steaming chicken soup helped dispel the cold.

We sang, and if there would have been more room, we would have danced like we did in Rabbi Segal's succah, but this pre-fab succah was rather small. Marvin told us what he had learned in day school about Succos. The four walls and the roof represented the Clouds of Glory, which encircled and protected the Israelites when they left Egypt. Hadassah asked the logical question: Why, then, is Succos not celebrated together with or right after Passover? Marvin said that his teacher explained that God wanted it to be evident that we were sitting in the succah because it is a mitzvah rather than because we just wanted to cool off. After Passover the weather is warm, and people may seek the shade of the succah for comfort. In the fall, no one seeks to cool off, and it is obvious that the succah serves only a mitzvah purpose. We could readily agree to that. We certainly were not sitting bundled up in the succah for comfort.

Marvin also said that the seven Patriarchs visit the succah and bless us. I remembered that Rabbi Segal had said that, and had pointed out that each night is dedicated to one of the Patriarchs. The first night is that of the Patriarch Abraham, which is especially significant for anyone with that name. Inasmuch as my Hebrew name is Avraham, I qualified as the guest of honor that night. Silently, I asked the Patriarch for his blessing.

We invited some friends for the second night, and I told them what Rabbi Segal had said, that the succah was a temporary dwelling which represented a person's temporary existence on earth, following which we return to our permanent home, which symbolizes the eternal world. The fact is that we celebrate Succos with great joy because it reinforces the concept of a permanent existence after our life on earth is over.

After the meal we went into the house to schmooze a bit in a warmer environment. One of our guests, Sherry, called me aside and thanked me for what I had said. She was undergoing treatment for breast cancer, and the thought that we can be happy rather than morose over our mortality was comforting. I felt I had to share with her why this was so important to me. I told her about my illness. She said she felt quite upbeat anyway, and the idea of an existence after death just added to her positive outlook.

It is amazing what sharing can do. Until now, no one other than Rabbi Segal and a few people at the office knew about my condition. It was actually a relief to talk about it to someone who had a similar condition and shared my concerns. We had a rather lengthy conversation. Sherry said that only her family and a few close friends were aware of her problem. She had been encouraged to attend a support group, but had been reluctant to do so. After our commiserating, she realized that it was comforting to share feelings with someone who understood.

How crazy the ego is! I was not willing to consider a support group the way Sherry did. Although it was illogical, I felt that being in a support group was something like sitting in the X-ray waiting room with a flimsy gown. It was sort of demeaning, an admission that I needed the help of others. I had made peace with my dependency on Evelyn, but I was not about to become dependent on a group of strangers for moral support. Maybe if there was a support group consisting of other top executives like myself it would be tolerable. I had to laugh at the kind of stupid thought I was capable of. But my stupidity notwithstanding, I dismissed the idea of a support group.

I did tell Sherry of my interest and research into immortality of the soul. I told her about Rabbi Segal and Rabbi Rabinowitz, and that these were good people to consult if she felt the need. I told her that it was normal to be anxious, and that the anxiety could be overcome. I told her how I had avoided driving through the tunnel for months because it reminded me of Dr. Harriman's remark, but that I overcame that and now drive through the tunnel without any anxiety.

I told Sherry that she could call me at any time if she felt the need to share. I realized that it would be OK for *her* to call *me* for moral support, but not for *me* to call *her*. After all, I was the founder of Silverman & Rabin, the largest Jewish law firm in the city.

My seventeen month period of being symptom-free and with favorable test results came to an abrupt end at my next appointment with Dr. Harriman. "Mr. Silverman," he said, "your tests show a recurrence of the disease."

Very foolishly I asked, "Are you sure?"

Dr. Harriman took no offense at this question. He was quite accustomed to patients reacting with denial. "I'm afraid so," he said.

"You have had an excellent remission with the medication protocol we used, with very minimal side effects. I believe we can get another remission using the same treatment with perhaps a slight modification. To use a more aggressive treatment would very likely give you more unpleasant side effects, and I don't feel this is called for now.

"I can also tell you that there is a promising new treatment on the horizon which will soon be available to us."

"You mean there may be light at the end of the tunnel?" I asked.

Dr. Harriman smiled. "Well, perhaps a flicker," he said. "What we are hoping for is longer remissions."

I made an appointment to begin the next course of treatment.

I went to my office, because I needed to think things through before telling Evelyn about the recurrence. She had shared in my illusion that I was cured. I also knew that I would get an "I told you so" from Adina.

I sat down behind my desk and tried to think, but the shattering of my dream had brought on a mood that blocked my thinking. Perhaps if I talked it through with Sherry, my mind would be less befuddled.

But how could I call Sherry? I was sitting in my leather judge's chair behind a massive walnut desk in a dignified, plush, executive office; am I going to call Sherry for help?

Then I said to myself, almost out loud, "Get off this ego trip! There must be something seriously wrong with you psychologically if you think it beneath your dignity to call Sherry." I decided to call her, and also to call Jeff, my psychologist friend. It was time to do something about my uncontrollable ego.

I reached Sherry immediately and told her about the recurrence, and that I felt crushed. I would like to be able to shake off this morbid feeling before I go home and tell Evelyn.

Sherry was very empathic, but what she said was like a teacher reprimanding a fourth grader. "Of course this is terribly upsetting to you, Alan. I can remember how I felt when I was told I had cancer. The world turned bleak for me. I wanted the doctor to send the slides to Sloan-Kettering. The pathologist may have been mistaken. I prayed that I would wake up and find it was only a bad dream, a nightmare. But the support of my wonderful family and the passing of time allowed me to accept reality and make the best of it."

Sherry continued, "I am not in denial of my disease. After I adjusted to the diagnosis of cancer, I rewrote my will and bought a cemetery plot. Statistically, I have a fifty per cent chance of a five-year survival, and that's not exactly a pleasant thought.

"I'm fifty eight. My mother died when she was forty-nine, and my father died two years later. 'Of a heart attack,' the doctors said. Baloney! He died of grief. I have now lived longer than my parents. I have two wonderful children and two beautiful grandchildren. I know that my son, Mendy, will say *kaddish* for me. I am not giving up by any means. I am not ready to die, but I'm not going to deny reality.

"I've enjoyed life, and I have no complaints. I am going to keep on living a full life. I am going to enjoy my kids and grandkids. I cooperate with the doctors and I pray to God for recovery. I'm not going to let the fear of dying ruin my life. Besides, if I don't live to a ripe old age, I'll be spared Alzheimer's disease.

"I'm sure you've put your affairs in order just like I have," Sherry said. "Go ahead with the next course of treatment. That's all you can do. The rest is in God's hands."

Wow! I was told off. Sherry hadn't impressed me as being capable of this attitude, but obviously, she was right.

I still had to make good on my decision to see Jeff, my psychologist friend. I called and told him that I wanted to see him professionally, and that although we were friends, I wanted to be billed as any other client. Jeff said, "Martha and I have been planning to rewrite our will. How about if we barter services?" I agreed, and made an appointment to meet with him.

I was glad I had talked with Sherry. My alarmed reaction and depressed mood had dissipated. I came home (and incidentally, I drove through the tunnel) and told Evelyn that Dr. Harriman said that there was another hurdle to overcome, and because my response to the treatment was so good, I should have another course of treatment. He also said that there was a promising new treatment that would soon be available. I thought that perhaps I should tell her about the advantage of avoiding Alzheimer's, but I decided against it. Evelyn knew this was a setback, but her attitude was positive, and that helped me considerably.

I met with Jeff and told him that I had become aware of my ego. I told him about my disease, and that I had been obsessed with the fear that when I died I would just go out of existence. Maybe that was an irrational fear, and maybe it was just another manifestation of my ego that I wanted to be around forever. Jeff said that the desire for an existence after death was not an ego thing, but rather an extension of the self-survival instinct, hence it is perfectly normal. As far as my ego was concerned, he said we could deal with that. "People with a good feeling about themselves, with healthy self-esteem, do not have an inflated ego. It is not unusual for people who are very gifted and have achieved much to nevertheless have low self-esteem. This is something we can address."

Jeff then said, "I never questioned that there is some kind of existence after death. For death to be an absolute finality of one's existence would make a mockery out of life. But just some kind of existence is not enough for me.

"I was not really interested much in reincarnation. It really makes little difference for me to know who I was in a previous existence if I had one, or who I might be next time around. It is a useless piece of information.

"But I am very interested in resurrection," Jeff said, and tears welled up in his eyes. He took a picture out of his wallet. "This is Jessica, the second of my children, who died of leukemia at age eleven." The tears rolled down his cheeks as he showed me a picture of a beautiful, smiling child with long, golden curls. "Jessie was everything a father could want in a daughter, bright, sweet, and gifted. She was an angel of a child, and I don't have the slightest doubt that she is an angel in heaven now."

Jeff kissed the picture gently and replaced it in his wallet. "Martha and I went for bereavement counseling. We knew we could never really adjust to losing her. I think that Martha made a better adjustment because she was more closely involved in tending to the other children, but I could find no peace. I had no problem being angry at God for not saving her, and I overcame that. We were most concerned that our prolonged grieving might impact on our other two children, who might feel that they are less important to us than Jessica was. My oldest son was thirteen, and his sharing in the grief would make it easier for him to understand. He loved his sister very much. But our younger son was only seven at the time, and his comprehension of what had happened was limited. We needed help with him.

"It's nine years now since Jessica died," Jeff said, wiping away his tears. "It is comforting for me to know that she is an angel in heaven, blissfully basking in the glory of God, as Rabbi Segal explained. I can be happy for her, but not for myself. I want to believe that some day I will be able to hold her again, to put my arms around her and kiss my lovely child. Can *neshamos* embrace and kiss? I don't think so, and that makes me sad.

"I want very much to believe in resurrection. I had hoped that Rabbi Rabinowitz would address it."

"Then let's go back to Rabbi Rabinowitz," I said.

When I left Jeff, I felt guilty about being an ingrate. I was blessed that my children would survive me. Nine years later, Jeff's wound was still so painful.

Jeff is a very level-headed person. His belief in the eternal existence of the soul was firm. For me, that would be enough. But Jeff's needs were different than mine. He knew that one day he would be reunited with his child, but did not know how, and this bothered him. Perhaps Rabbi Rabinowitz could help.

R abbi Rabinowitz appeared happy to see us. *"Shalom aleichem,"* he said. "Did our conversation last time stimulate new questions?" he asked.

I said, "Rabbi, I think you can help us most if you know why we are really here. It is not just curiosity.

"About a year and a half ago, I was diagnosed with non-Hodgkins lymphoma, in a rather serious form. I underwent chemotherapy with an excellent result of a seventeen month remission. I have recently had a recurrence, and I will be getting a second course of chemotherapy.

"Prior to my illness, I had never considered issues such as mortality, immortality, life after death, and so on. I am not philosophically inclined, and my law practice occupied all of my thinking. The fact that I have a disease for which there is no known cure caused me to consider these issues. The thought that death is an absolute finality and that I would simply fade into oblivion compounded my normal fears of dying. I became obsessed with this thought, and I have been seeking assurances that in some way, a person continues to exist after death.

"Rabbi Segal has been very helpful in my coming to believe that we have a *neshamah* that is eternal, and that death is a change from one kind of existence to another, but that we do continue to exist. Frankly, during the months of my remission, when I allowed myself to think I had been cured, I was quite at ease with my belief in the afterlife. Now that my security has been shaken by my relapse, my concern is more than academic, and I could certainly use some reinforcement of belief in an afterlife."

Jeff said, "My question is a bit different. I never doubted an afterlife. I lost a beautiful child to leukemia when she was eleven years old. I am firm in my belief that she exists in heaven, perhaps as an angel just as she was in her lifetime." Jeff took out the picture of Jessica and showed it to Rabbi Rabinowitz.

"But I have this insatiable longing and hope to be reunited with her," Jeff said. "I cannot conceive how *neshamos* unite. All I can think of is how much I loved her and how wonderful it was when I held her in my arms. I yearn to embrace her once again. I know that in the *Amidah* we assert our belief that those who died will be resurrected. This would be more comforting if I knew that I would have her once again just as she was. But the idea of the dead coming to life once again is not easy to accept. It is easier for me to understand resurrection as the living of the *neshamah* once again. But what about the body?" Jeff pointed to the picture. "Will I ever see her this way again, even if it's a thousand years from now?"

Rabbi Rabinowitz was deeply moved, and tears welled up in his eyes. "Yes, my dear friend," he said. "You will be able to embrace your child again.

"There is much discussion among our foremost theologians on what is meant by the term *Olam Haba*, the world to come. Clearly it refers to something in the future, but to what? Some authorities say that it refers to a spiritual world, to heaven, which is each person's 'world to come.' Others say that *Olam Haba* refers to the future era after the coming of Moshiach and the ultimate Redemption, which will be followed by the resurrection of the dead.

"There is also some disagreement whether resurrection means that the bodies of people who once lived will be restored to life, or whether there will be some kind of spiritual resurrection, the nature of which is imprecise.

"The prevailing opinion is that of Ramban, a thirteenth century Torah commentator who was well-versed both in halachah and kabbalah, and he is most emphatic that resurrection means a restoration of the physical body as well as the spirit. Ramban insists that the Biblical phrase 'when I open your graves' in Ezekiel 37 is to be taken literally.

"This is also evident in the Talmud, which relates a dialogue between a non-believer who challenged a sage on the impossibility of the dead coming to life. The sage responded, 'You have no problem in accepting that people who never existed come into existence. You see this with every birth of a child. Is it not logical that if those who never existed can come into existence, then certainly those who once did exist can return to existence?' This is clearly a statement of physical resurrection.

"The Talmud also states that there is a tiny bone in the spinal column that never disintegrates, and that from this bone, the person will be resurrected. If resurrection were only a spiritual phenomenon, why would it necessitate the survival of a body part?

"Of course, 'people who never existed coming into existence' does not present a challenge only because birth of a new person is a regular occurrence, whereas no one has witnessed a dead person returning to life. That is the simple difference between a natural phenomenon and a miracle. No one thinks that it is a miracle if you bury a tiny seed in the

ground, and after it disintegrates it sprouts a tree that produces abundant fruit for year after year. Imagine someone
who was born and raised in an arid desert and who had never
heard of nor seen the growth issuing from the planting of a
seed in the ground. If he were told that burying a tiny seed in
the ground will give rise to a fruit-bearing tree, he would say
that this is absurd. It is very much a miracle, but we accept it
as a natural phenomenon. This natural phenomenon was set
in motion by God at the time of Creation. In the Thirteen
Principles of Faith, Rambam uses the expression that resurrection of the dead will occur 'whenever the wish emanates
from the Creator.' At Creation, it was the wish of the Creator
that a tiny seed should disintegrate and produce a tree. At a
time in the future, it will be the wish of the Creator that a
body that has been buried should come to life. That phenomenon will be as natural then as the growth of a tree is
now."

Rabbi Rabinowitz continued, "Actually, modern science
has diminished some of the miraculous character of resurrection. With the amazing discovery of the genetic code of DNA,
scientists have been able to clone. As you know, DNA is
exquisitely unique. No two persons on earth have exactly the
same DNA. I don't know what previous generations made of
the Talmudic statement that resurrection will come from a
tiny bone that survives, but given our current knowledge, all
that is necessary is to have a single cell which contains the
genetic code, and from which it is possible to form a whole
being. And if even a single cell does not survive, why, God in
His omniscience knows the genetic code of every human
being. It is really not that striking a miracle for God to use that
genetic code to form the same person who was once alive.

"And so, my friend," Rabbi Rabinowitz said, pointing to
the picture of Jessica, "it is hardly so great a challenge to logic
to believe that one day in the future, you will once again

embrace this lovely child.

"I must add something," Rabbi Rabinowitz continued. "There was a great sage in Israel who would stand up out of respect whenever a mother passed by with a Down Syndrome child. He said that a *neshamah* comes down to an earthly existence in order to fulfill its mission by performing the mitzvos of the Torah. If a *neshamah* comes into the world in a person whose limitations preclude him from doing much, it is because that *neshamah* has already neared completion, and there is not much more that it must do. This sage believed that a Down Syndrome child bore a special *neshamah,* and he would stand up out of respect for it.

"The Baal Shem Tov said that this also holds true for a child that is taken from the world prematurely. That child's *neshamah* neared its completion, and there was no need for it to tarry longer in this world. You bore a child with a special *neshamah.*"

Jeff stood up, threw his arms around Rabbi Rabinowitz, hugged him tightly and broke into tears. The rabbi and I cried tears of pain and joy along with him.

After we regained our composure, Rabbi Rabinowitz turned to me and said, "And now, Mr. Silverman, let's address the question of the existence of the *neshamah* after death."

I said, "Never mind, Rabbi. I had never relinquished my belief. I had just wanted it reinforced. There could be no greater reinforcement than what you have just provided."

T he second course of treatment was a bit rougher than the first course, but I only missed one day at the office. I did tire more easily and went home early a few times, but essentially my life was normal.

Chanukah was approaching. We had never had a Chanukah party of our own, and it was high time we did. Almost everyone we invited was there. Of course, our children were all there. Sherry and Melvin and three other couples came. Naively, I had invited Rabbi Rabinowitz, who politely declined. I did not know that chassidic rebbes do not usually attend parties at other people's homes. Rabbi Rabinowitz invited me to attend his candle lighting one night.

We had a great time at the party. Evelyn's potato *latkes* were superb, thin, crispy, and delicious, served with apple sauce or sour cream. She kept going back into the kitchen to make another batch, because no sooner did she bring out a platterful than they were consumed. Even Adina broke her sacred regimen and ate fried *latkes*. I recalled that when I was a child, Bubby also made *latkes* out of kasha, buckwheat, fried in *schmaltz*. Adina had an expression of horror on her face. "You mean you ate them?" she said. I said, "You bet, and plenty of them." I knew what was going through her mind: buckwheat *latkes* fried in *schmaltz* were probably the cause of my disease, but she wisely said nothing.

After we lit the candles, Marvin told the story of Chanukah, relating the triumph of the Macabees and the miracle of the single vial of undefiled oil burning for eight days. We sang the traditional Chanukah songs and played *dreidel*. As always, one of the players had all the luck. When the game was over, all the coins were put into the *tzedakah* box. Our spirits were high. Sherry said that an enjoyable evening like this was at least as effective as chemotherapy. She promised to host the Chanukah party next year. Silently, I said, "Amen."

After everyone left, Adina and Jack remained. Adina then told us the good news: she was expecting a baby in June. Evelyn and I were thrilled.

On the fourth night of Chanukah I took Rabbi Rabinowitz up on his invitation, and Jeff joined me. I had no idea of what to expect. The candle lighting was in his little synagogue, which was crowded with his followers, standing room only. Most of the people were bearded and had side curls, but strangely, I did not feel out of place. Young boys were standing on tables. Everyone was waiting for Rabbi Rabinowitz, whom they referred to as "the rebbe," to enter.

The room was alive with buzzing, everybody holding conversation with his neighbor. Suddenly there was a total silence. Everyone's eyes were fixed on the door that was just opening. Rabbi Rabinowitz entered, clad in a colorful robe. He walked to his place near the lectern, turned around and scanned the crowd, nodding recognition to several people. When he noticed me and Jeff, he smiled and motioned to us to come near. The milling crowd promptly drew aside to form a path for us. As we approached him, I felt that everyone must be thinking, "Who in the world are these two guys?" Rabbi Rabinowitz shook hands with us and had us stand near him.

I was accustomed to a simple brief lighting of the candles. Not so with Rabbi Rabinowitz. He was holding a thick book from which he was silently reading while swaying slowly to and fro. The silence in the room was deafening. He took a beeswax candle which he lit from another candle. With his eyes closed in deep meditation, he recited the blessings, then lit the wicks in his oil menorah. He sat back for several minutes of silent meditation, and then began chanting, which I later learned was from the Psalms. The chassidim all joined in. After the singing was over, he turned around and addressed the crowd.

"As you know," Rabbi Rabinowitz said, "Chanukah was the occasion of two miraculous events. There was the military victory of a small group of Jews who led a rebellion against the Syrian Greeks who had attempted to suppress observance of Judaism. The triumph of a handful of warriors against the mighty army of Antiochus was clearly a miraculous occurrence.

"When the Macabees regained the Holy Temple and wished to renew the Divine service, they found only a single vial of oil that had not been defiled in pagan rituals. This was enough to burn in the Menorah for only one night, but it miraculously lasted for eight days, until fresh oil was available.

"Of the two miracles," the rabbi said, "one was physical, the military victory, and the other was spiritual, the sustaining light of the Menorah. We celebrate Chanukah not by parades and banners of the military triumph, but for the miracle of the Menorah.

"As significant as the military triumph was, it was not of long duration. The Holy Land was repeatedly conquered by foreign powers, and the Jews were driven into exile. What has prevailed throughout the millennia is the spiritual miracle, that of the menorah, and that is how we celebrate Chanukah.

"As with our nation, so with every individual. We have physical triumphs, as we advance ourselves economically with better homes, better furnishings, and better cars. While these serve a purpose, they are limited in time, as are our physical lives. But there is a spiritual component within us which is Divine, a part of Almighty God Himself. This is the *neshamah*. Very appropriately, the Chanukah celebration is one of lighting a lamp, for as the Torah says, 'the *neshamah* of man is the lamp of God.'

"We begin with a single, tiny flicker of light that increases every day. Whereas the physical is static at best, and may even be lost as the physical land of Israel was lost, the spiritual can grow and grow. The tiny flicker can expand to give much light. It is to our spiritual component that we must dedicate our attention, because the spiritual is our eternity.

"The Chanukah lights are of special significance. When Rome overran Jerusalem, they sacked the Holy Temple. You have seen pictures of the Arch of Titus which stood on the road leading to the Roman Forum. The frieze on the Arch depicted soldiers carrying off the Menorah, with the inscription 'Judea Capta.' Who at that time would have thought that the tiny state of Judea would ever come to life again? Who at that time would have doubted that the mighty Roman Empire that ruled the world would dominate the world forever? But today, Judea is very much alive. And if you visit Rome, you can walk on the ruins of the Forum. The once mighty empire is a historic relic. Rome carried off one Menorah, and tonight millions of menorahs shine in Jewish homes.

"Although the spiritual in Judaism is dominant, the physical is not neglected. The Divine promise is that the Land of Israel will once again come alive. Jerusalem will blossom again, in all its glory and beauty. May we merit the day when the ultimate Redemption returns us to our Land and to our Temple, when we rejoice with both our physical and spiritual salvation. Amen."

At a signal from the rabbi, the crowd broke into jubilant song. Somehow, circles of dancing people formed in the crowded room. The rabbi took me by the hand, and I pulled Jeff into the dancing circle.

When we left, Jeff said, "Did you hear what the rabbi said to me? Chanukah represents both the physical and spiritual miracles, and there will ultimately be a physical restoration as well as a spiritual. He said that what is true of the nation is true of the individual. For me, too, there will be a physical as well as spiritual resurrection."

I responded, "I was sure he was addressing me. He said that a tiny flicker of light can expand to great brightness. What Dr. Harriman said to me was that there was a flicker of light. But that's all I need. That flicker can become the brightness I am hoping for."

Jeff and I returned home, profoundly enriched by Rabbi Rabinowitz's Chanukah message.

J eff and I became close friends, too close for him to be my therapist. He recommended another psychologist to help me deal with my inflated ego.

I recognized that I was indeed down on myself, partially because there were aspects of myself that I did not like. For example, I knew that I was an angry person. Although I had mellowed at home, I could still explode at the office when someone did anything detrimental to a particular litigation or transaction. I knew this was not a good character trait, but my reactions were impulsive. That was me, and I could not change.

Rabbi Segal's classes were very helpful. Essentially, *The Path of the Just* is all about change. Rabbi Segal explained that the author's thesis that we were placed in the world to do God's will was really nothing more than to change ourselves.

"Man," Rabbi Segal said, "comes into the world full of negative traits. In the Book of Job the expression is, 'Man is born as a wild mule.' It is of this wild mule that the Torah requires the extreme transformation, to become a holy, spiritual being. Moses said that we are to 'cleave unto God.' 'How can we do that?' the Talmud asks. By emulating the Divine attributes. 'Just as God is compassionate and merciful, slow to anger, and forgiving, so must we become compassionate and merciful, slow to anger, and forgiving.'

"What can bring about so radical a change, from a wild mule to a holy, spiritual being? The only possible way this can be achieved is by following the Torah. People may try to better themselves without the Torah, but that is very much like trying to assemble a complex apparatus using one's own wisdom. When all else fails and one is totally frustrated, one reads the manufacturer's instruction booklet that was included with the apparatus.

"God created man as a 'wild mule,' and provided him with the instructions needed to become a holy, spiritual being. Observing Torah is not doing God a favor. The Talmud says that how an animal is slaughtered makes no real difference to God. The mitzvos were given to refine people, and by following the mitzvos with the intent to improve one's character, a person can become holy and spiritual."

Rabbi Segal related some anecdotes of great personalities who were indeed holy and spiritual people. They, too, had come into the world as "wild mules."

Rabbi Segal said that his grandfather had studied in Poland under a sage known as the Chafetz Chaim. His grandfather had told him stories of this extraordinary person. The Chafetz Chaim did not wish to be supported by public funds, so he kept a little store open long enough to earn just for his needs of that day. Then he would close shop and devote himself to Torah study, with perfect trust in God that tomorrow he would be able to earn enough for that day.

This great sage, his grandfather said, was the paragon of humility. Although he was revered by the entire Jewish world, he was so unassuming that one could not identify him in a crowd. He dressed simply, without the elegant apparel that often depicts a leader.

I thought of my huge walnut desk and leather judge's chair, and the layout of my office which announced, "I am the boss." Humility was something that I needed to work on.

Rabbi Segal's grandfather told him that one day the sage asked him for a favor. He had just received a delivery from the printer of many copies of a book that he had written. He wanted to examine each book, page by page, to make certain that he would not be selling defective merchandise, because that would be tantamount to theft. He was unable to examine each book personally, and he asked Rabbi Segal's grandfather, who was then a youth of fifteen, to help him. "My grandfather said that he sat with the sage for hours, checking every book. Whenever a defect was discovered, the sage set it aside, and was overjoyed that he had avoided taking someone's money for damaged merchandise."

As we continued our study and discussions, I realized that I was wrong in thinking myself to be a fixed entity. If I had an angry streak, that was the 'wild mule' in me that had not been tamed. How could I have any self-esteem when I was still partially a wild mule?

I knew I had a long way to go, but at least I was on the right track.

It occurred to me that perhaps others in the office could benefit from learning something about spirituality. Rabbi Segal suggested a local Torah scholar. I arranged for lunch to be brought in once a week, and during the lunch hour this young man would lead a discussion on spirituality. A goodly portion of the office staff took advantage of this opportunity.

On my birthday, the kids all came with their gifts. Hadassah's birthday card read, "Last year I said you were the best Daddy in the whole world. This year, you're better than the best."

Why is it that we don't think about how we should live until we start getting ready to die?

I was amused the other day when I saw a sign on the approach to the tunnel: it would be closed from 10 PM to 6 AM for installation of new lights. They were going to make the tunnel brighter. My tunnel had already become brighter.

One day when I was at Dr. Harriman's office for treatment, the nurse who was about to administer my intravenous medication said, "I like dealing with you, Mr. Silverman."

"Why is that?" I asked.

"Because you're always pleasant and smiling. This is not the happiest place to work. Many people are morose, which is understandable. They often complain about side effects of the medication, and I can't blame them. We try our best to make our patients comfortable. I'd like to be able to lift up their spirits, but I don't know how. But I've never seen you like that, and it's refreshing. Do you mind if I ask you what's your secret?"

"What's my secret?" I thought. "What *is* my secret?" Then I said, "Until I developed lymphoma, I thought I was living right. In the past two years I have come to realize that I had really not been living like a human being at all. I was just like one of those ants that you see rushing around an ant hill. The ant probably thinks it is doing the most important thing in the world. Look out the window once and you'll see what looks pretty much like a bunch of ants in very busy activity, running helter-skelter around the ant hill.

"My disease shocked me into reality. I realized that I wasn't really living right at all, and in the past two years, I've been learning a great deal about how to really live. When you're busy learning how to live, you don't think much about dying."

"I just wish other people thought that way," the nurse said.

I had been having occasional phone conversations with Sherry. Her upbeat attitude was good for me. One day she said, "You know what I'm doing? I'm volunteering at the hospice. It's been a very rewarding experience. You ought to give it a try."

"I'll think about it." I said, lying through my teeth. I had no intention of volunteering at a hospice. I had made an adjustment to life, and if I wasn't going to live forever, I was going to enjoy every day of my life. Like I said to the nurse, I was too busy learning how to live to think about dying. The hospice would reverse all that.

I happened to mention to Jeff that Sherry was volunteering at a hospice. Jeff said, "There's two ways to look at that. It may be a counter-phobic defense. That's when a person who is afraid of something runs right into the situation he fears. It's a kind of denial mechanism, essentially saying, 'I'm *not* afraid of this.' Sherry may have had the unpleasant thought, 'May I someday end up in a hospice?' One way to react is to tackle it. 'See! There's nothing to fear about a hospice.'

"But it may also be," Jeff said, "that she is doing it out of a sincere desire to help other people with whom she can identify."

I said, "Sherry invited me to join her. I am turned off by the idea. Do you think I'm being phobic?"

"Not every phobia is pathologic. A phobia of enclosed space can be dysfunctional if it prevents one from entering an elevator. Avoiding a hospice is not really dysfunctional.

"But I will tell you this much," Jeff said. "My daughter Jessica was in the hospital for weeks at a time. When we visited her, the nurses would ask us to spend some time with some of the children who didn't have many visitors. It was really rewarding to be able to cheer up some of the kids. They would see other children who had frequent visitors and they were envious of them."

Jeff continued, "I'm not telling you to volunteer at the hospice, but I'm sure that some of the elderly people never have any visitors."

I said, "OK, I'll think about it."

At one of the subsequent study groups, Rabbi Segal spoke about the great mitzvah of *tzedakah*. Then he said, "The Talmud says that *gemilas chassadim*, acts of kindness, surpass even *tzedakah* in merit. Whereas *tzedakah* is done with one's belongings, acts of kindness are done with one's self. Whereas *tzedakah* is given only to the poor, acts of kindness can be done for the wealthy as well."

After the session was over, I said to Jeff, "That does it. I'm going to have to go to the hospice."

I called Sherry, who was overjoyed that I would go with her.

The hospice was esthetically very pleasant. The décor was homelike, comfortable, and cheerful, and each patient had a private room. Several people were watching TV in the lounge. It made me feel uneasy. "They're watching TV, waiting to die," I thought.

Sherry took me into one of the rooms and introduced me to a patient, whose eyes lit up when she saw Sherry. "I'm so glad you're here," she said. "I want to hear the rest of the book."

Sherry explained, "Thelma has macular degeneration and cannot read. She used to be an English instructor in a university. Many of the books she is interested in are not available on audio-tapes, so I read to her. I'll be back in a little while," Sherry said to Thelma.

Sherry then walked me down the hall to see the dining area. I thought I heard someone call out my name. I looked around and saw a man gesture to me. "Alan, is that you?"

I went over to the man, whom I recognized, with some difficulty, as Mr. Zagermacher. That wasn't his real name, but because he repaired watches, he was known by the Yiddish equivalent of "watch maker," which is Zagermacher.

Zagermacher must have been at least eighty. In addition to repairing watches, he used to assist the Talmud Torah teacher in preparing kids for their Bar Mitzvah, and I had been one of his students. As the years passed I would see him on occasion when I would bring a watch in to repair. He also sold watches, and when I entered law school I bought my wrist-alarm from him.

"I'm surprised you recognized me after all these years," I said.

"My body isn't much good," Zagermacher said, "but Denks to Gutt my mind is still sharp. I never forget a face."

Zagermacher said that he had developed a form of leukemia fifteen years ago. A very mild form of leukemia, which was controlled by treatment. However, in the last six months it had disabled him. He was widowered and was living alone. He has one son who had settled in Israel many years ago. The old age home would not accept him because of his disease, and so he has been in the hospice.

"I'm so glad to see you, Alan," he said. I've made some friends here, but I don't know anyone from way back."

I sat with Zagermacher, who wanted to know everything about me. He knew my parents, but did not know they had died. "They were good people," he said. "I remember your father picking you up from Talmud Torah. You had a beautiful Bar Mitzvah. I was proud of you."

I held Zagermacher's hand and said, "That's because you prepared me well."

"You weren't exactly happy being in Talmud Torah after school when your friends were out there playing football," he said. We both laughed.

"Oy, thank you, Alan. It's been a long time since I had something to laugh about."

Zagermacher said, "Come with me." He drove his wheelchair to a room, and I followed him. "Open that drawer, please," he said. He asked me to hand him a manila envelope.

Zagermacher showed me some pictures. "This is my only son, Yonah, with his wife, Naomi. He lives in Haifa. He has four children. See? Here they are. This is Batya, the oldest, with her husband, Binyamin, and their two children, Yonah's grandchildren. Yes, I am a great-grandfather. Then comes Noam and his wife, Gila, and their son, Avishai. And this is Shalom, named after my wife's father, and Vered, Yonah's youngest. I had hoped he would name one of the girls after my mother. Her name was Yenta Kaila. They don't give such names in Israel. Especially Yenta. In Yiddish a 'yenta' is a gossiper. Why did they give such names? I don't know. Nu, what can you do? They should all be well.

"My son's name is Yonah Zamir," Zagermacher said. "In Hebrew 'Zamir' means 'singer.' When Yonah moved to Israel he changed his name from Singer to Zamir. Nu, also good. Last year he was here for a few days to see me, but, you know, it's not easy to come from Israel often. "

I had never known that Zagermacher's real name was Singer. We talked a good bit, and there were some things we reminisced about.

Sherry came to fetch me, and I said goodbye to Zagermacher. "You'll come back, Alan, yes?"

I squeezed Zagernmacher's hand. "Of course," I said, then added jokingly, "And if I bring you my watch, you'll fix it?"

Zagermacher laughed. "You just get me my tools and my magnifying glass, and you bet I'll fix it. I told you, the body is no good, but the head is like a young boy."

As we left the hospice, I said to Sherry, "Thank you. You've made my day."

I told Evelyn about my experience at the hospice. She was very moved. "I think I'll volunteer at the hospice, too," she said.

I could not get Zagermacher out of my mind. Here was a man who had lived a decent life and deserved a pleasant old age. So what does he have? Nothing. I was undoubtedly the first visitor he had had since he had entered the hospice. How does he feel when he sees visitors coming to the other residents day after day, but no one comes to see him? His only son lives in Israel and does not have the financial resources to make frequent trips to the United States. The man has never seen any of his grandchildren or great-grandchildren.

Who knows that Zagermacher is in the hospice? Most of his peers are either gone or housebound. Can a person live without anyone taking an interest in him?

What motivates Zagermacher to get out of bed in the morning? What does he have to look forward to in the day? The hospice staff are indeed very considerate, but let's face it, they are paid employees. There is nothing to bond them to Zagermacher other than their duty to care for him. I don't think I could live like that. Life like that would be meaningless for me.

Perhaps it is the instinct for self-survival that keeps a person going. Maybe that is the same instinct that is propelling me to look for the afterlife: a wish to survive, not to ever go out of existence.

It occurred to me that there must be a number of students whom Zagermacher had tutored for Bar-Mitzvah. Maybe they could visit him. I called the local Anglo-Jewish weekly newspaper and put in a small ad: "If you were a student of Aaron Singer (a.k.a. 'Zagermacher'), please call 444-6666." It was a long shot, but maybe someone would respond.

The following Sunday, I went to the hospice. Zagermacher was happy to see me. I didn't know what to bring him. I remembered that he used to smoke cigarettes, but there was no smoking in the hospice. I brought him a small box of chocolates. I don't know how long it had been since he had received a gift of any kind.

We small-talked a bit, and then I couldn't control my curiosity. "Mr. Singer," I said, "how do you get along here in the hospice?"

"What's to get along?" he said. "The people here are nice." He was silent for a few moments, then said (I wish I could relate it to you in his quaint Yiddish-English), "Alan, you know what kind of place this is. Everybody here has cancer or some other terrible disease. Some are very young, like forty-five. They have small children coming to visit them. It is a heartache.

"Me? I'm going to be eighty-six. I've lived a good life. Some people here haven't had a good chance to even live. A shame.

"I came to America in 1924. Coolidge was president. I was fifteen. I had my Bar-Mitzvah back home in Bobruisk. My father was killed in a pogrom when I was seven. My mother had an uncle who had come to America years before, and he brought my mother and me here.

"My mother was good at sewing, so she worked in a tailor shop. What's a fifteen-year-old boy going to do? English I couldn't talk. My uncle was a butcher and he wanted to teach me to be a butcher like him. I tried for a few months, but I didn't like it.

"Since I was little, I liked to *potschke* (putter) with things. Take apart, put together, you know. Across from my uncle's butcher shop was a watchmaker. I used to sit in his shop and watch him. A very nice man. He saw I was interested. He was friends with my uncle and he knew I have no father. He asked me, did I want he should teach me watchmaking? I was so happy. 'Sure,' I said. He showed me all about watches. I loved him, and I loved to *potschke* with watches. There were some old clocks that were no good. I took some parts from one and some parts from another and I put together a clock that worked. My! He couldn't believe it. Soon he let me help him fix watches.

"I made a few dollars, but that was not enough. I went to some jewelers and told them about our watchmaking shop. Soon I brought in business and I was busy. I started making good money.

"After a few years, my boss says, 'Aaron, it's time for me to retire. You can take over the shop, and I'll come in to help. You give me half of what you make. OK?' 'It's a deal,' I said."

I could see how pleased Zagermacher was to tell his life story to someone, and I was eager to listen.

"Now I was making enough money to be a *baalabus* (head of a household). I married Gittel, a wonderful woman. I expanded the business to fix umbrellas, too.

"Gittel's father gave us enough money to buy a *haiske* (a little house). We were happy, thank God ('Denks Gutt' is what he said). We had a little *boychik,* Yonah, named after my father.

"All my life I had an honest business. I never charged too much. People liked me, and I had plenty customers. But I was missing a little bit the Yiddish, so I started helping out in the Talmud Torah, teaching boys Bar-Mitzvah.

"Yonah's class went to Israel for a visit. He worked that summer on a kibbutz and he liked it. Next year he went again, and he said, 'Pa, I'm going to live in Israel.' So what should I say, No? He finished high school and went to Israel. He works for the government. Much money he doesn't make, but Denks Gutt, he has a good family. I showed you the pictures, yes?"

I said, "Yes, you did. Beautiful grandchildren and great-grandchildren."

"Gittel and me was married fifty-six years," Zagermacher said. "She was good to me and I was good to her. No one can say different. Eight years ago she died. So I shouldn't be happy I had her for fifty-six years? How many people have a happy marriage for fifty-six years, huh?

"So you think I don't understand what's happening in this place? I talk with some of the people. Most are afraid of dying. What's to be afraid of? Tell me, Alan, it's possible to be afraid of something you don't know?

"One time my watchmaker boss was joking and he said, 'There's nothing so terrible about dying. It's when they put you away and walk away leaving you alone that's no good.' But it's no joke, Alan. People are afraid of being alone, that's why they're afraid of dying. But I'm already alone, so what's to be afraid of?"

Zagermacher's words pierced my heart. To be so alone that one doesn't fear death is tragic.

"Besides," Zagermacher said, "you know what it says in *Tehillim* (Psalms), 'When I walk through the shadow of death, I am not afraid, because God is with me.' So, God took care of me almost eighty-six years when I am living, He can take care of me after I die."

I remained silent. What is there to say after that?

Zagermacher broke the silence. "Nu, Alan, when you'll be eighty-six you'll understand."

"Eighty-six?" I thought. "I'll be happy to reach sixty and be at Marvin's Bar-Mitzvah."

"Alan," Zagermacher said. "I can ask you a favor?"

"Of course," I said. "Anything."

"You're a lawyer, yes?"

"That's right," I said.

"When Yonah was here," he said, "he arranged with a lawyer to take care of my house, so when I die, it belongs to him. The lawyer is Ben Goldman. I don't know him. I'd like you should talk with him and make sure everything is right."

I said, "Ben Goldman is a very fine lawyer. You can trust him."

"Now there is two tenants, upstairs and downstairs. I think it's better to sell the house and give the money to Yonah. No?"

"I'll talk with Ben Goldman," I said. "But tell me, how did you know I was a lawyer?"

Zagermacher smiled and said, "I told you the *sechel* (mind) is still good. Just like new. I remember you came in to buy a wrist watch with an alarm. I asked you why you needed it, and you said that you are going into law school and you needed an alarm to make sure you won't miss class in the morning." He pointed to his forehead. "I remember everything, Denks Gutt."

I was amazed. I laughed, squeezed Zagermacher's hand, and left.

So, my Bar-Mitzvah teacher was a lay philosopher! I was not convinced of his point that you cannot be afraid of something you do not know. It is commonplace that children are afraid of the dark even though they had never been hurt in the dark. I think that there is an instinctive fear of the unknown, and when you cannot see anything, your environment is unknown. With all due respect to Zagermacher, I think that the fear of death is the fear of the unknown. Maybe if I knew more about the afterlife, I wouldn't fear dying. Although I have come to believe in an afterlife, I have no idea of what it is like, and I still fear the unknown.

I did get two responses to my ad. One was from Alexander Burns, who is the head of a local brokerage firm, and the other was from Arthur Levin, a dentist. I knew them casually. I don't remember them from Talmud Torah. They are probably a few years younger than I am.

I told them both that Zagermacher was in the hospice, that he was very alert, and very much alone. His only son lives in

Israel. He has no local relatives, and his peers were either gone or housebound. I thought it would be good if they would visit him. Given his keen memory, he is sure to remember them. I knew they were both very busy, but perhaps they could visit him on a Sunday morning. They both agreed, and I suggested we all three meet Sunday morning at the hospice.

On Sunday morning the three of us met. I ushered them into Zagermacher's room. "You've got some visitors," I said. "Former students of yours. Here is Arthur Levin, and this is Alex Burns."

Zagermacher sized up the two, then slapped his hand against his face. "Oy, Guttenu (dear God)," he said. "What kind of Alex Burns? He's Sender Baruchovitz!'

Alex laughed. "You're right, Mr. Singer. But how many people would invest their money in a brokerage firm 'Sender Baruchovitz & Company?' So, for business purposes, it's Alexander Burns."

Zagermacher said, "The sign on my shop was 'Goldschmidt Watch Repair. You take your time, but bring us your watches.' Goldschmidt was the name of the owner before me. OK for watch repair but maybe not for brokerage. Nu! And you, Levin, could stay Levin?"

Art Levin said, "I'm a dentist, Mr. Singer. Everybody knows that Jewish doctors and dentists are the best. Do you remember me, Mr. Singer?"

"Ay, ay!" Zagermacher said. "Like I told Alan, I never forget. Levin, I should tell you that your Bar-Mitzvah (the Torah reading for the week of your thirteenth birthday) *parashas Vayikra*. Maybe you still remember?" Zagermacher began singing the words of the *haftarah* (the portion of the Prophets that he had taught Levin).

We all laughed heartily. "I can't believe you remember," Art said.

"You were all good boys," Zagermacher said. "Bernstein, you remember what happened on your Bar-Mitzvah?"

"Do I remember?" Alex said. "Could I ever forget? It was on a beautiful day in June. The *kiddush* (collation) was set up outside in the back of the *shul*. All of a sudden a rainstorm came from nowhere, and the whole *kiddush* was ruined. My mother was brokenhearted, and I cried so hard."

"Nu, and was it such a tragedy?" Zagermacher said. "So now you remember about it and you can laugh. Here in this place is no laughing. Here is *tzoros* (trouble). But a rained-out *kiddush* is no big *tzoros*."

Alex said, "I have a confession to make, Mr. Singer. One time, when you went out, you left your pack of cigarettes on the table, and I stole two of them. I smoked one of them and I coughed so hard that I threw the other one away."

"So you didn't become a smoker?" Zagermacher said.

"I never picked up a cigarette again," Alex said.

"So you had more brains than your teacher. You never were a *goniff* (thief) anymore after that? So you learned your lesson, and you can be honest in business.

"I'm so glad you came, boys," Zagermacher said. "If you got time, you can come back."

After we left the building, I said to Art and Alex, "I checked with the records in the hospice office. Zagermacher will be eighty-six in two months. I got the address of his son from the records. What do you say we all three pitch in and buy a ticket for his son and a grandchild to come for his birthday?"

"Great idea," they agreed. I said I would take care of it.

I don't recall when I ever felt as good as that day.

I contacted Zagermacher's son, Yonah Zamir, and told him about our offer. He was thrilled. He had hoped to visit his father, but simply could not afford it. He was overjoyed that he could bring one of the grandchildren along.

Bernstein (Burns) and Levin contacted several of their friends whom Zagermacher had tutored, and all agreed to visit him. It seemed that Zagermacher was going to have more visitors than any other patient in the hospice.

One day, as I was reviewing *Path of the Just*, I noticed that Luzzato referred to ten steps of spirituality, leading to resurrection. I quickly turned to the end of the book, but was disappointed to find only a few sentences on resurrection, which did not satisfy my curiosity.

At the next session I mentioned this to Rabbi Segal. Incidentally, I told him all about my experience at the hospice and Zagermacher. Rabbi Segal said that this was an extraordinary mitzvah of *gemilas chesed*, and that not only did I merit great reward for my personal acts, but even more because I had brought several other people to participate in the mitzvah. "The Talmud states that when God first appeared to the Patriarch Abraham, it was to visit him when he was recovering from his circumcision at age ninety-nine. Visiting the sick in a way that comforts them is emulating God's attributes.

"Why doesn't Luzzato elaborate on resurrection of the dead?" Rabbi Segal said. "It is because he is concentrating on the resurrection of the living.

"The Talmud says that righteous or just people are considered to be alive even after they have died, whereas the wicked are considered dead even when they are physically alive.

"The Torah says, 'You who cling to your God, you are all alive today.' In his last words to the Israelites, Moses says, 'See, I have placed before you today the life and the good, and the death and the evil. That which I command you today, to love your God, to walk in His ways, to observe His commandments, His decrees, and His ordinances, then you will live. And you shall choose life, so that you will live.'

"Moses repeatedly identifies life," Rabbi Segal continued, "with walking in the ways of God and observing His commandments. This is because Moses is defining life for us.

"The human being is a composite creature, comprised of an animal body and a Divine soul. Animals operate totally by bodily instinct. They do what their bodies demand. They cannot defy a bodily urge. All their actions are self-centered. If a human being acts only in a way to gratify his physical desires, then he is living an essentially animal life. His life becomes human only when he rises above self-centeredness.

"That is why the Talmud states that the wicked, who are totally driven by self-gratification, are considered dead even when they are alive. Yes, they breathe and move about, but so do animals. Their uniquely human component of life, the neshamah, is dead. On the other hand, the righteous who live according to the word of God are always alive, even after the body dies.

"There is a notable book of chassidic philosophy, *Tanya*, in which the author states that the chasm between mortal man and Infinite God is so vast, that it cannot be bridged in any way other than that provided by God, which is spelled out in the Torah. He points out that the word 'mitzvah,' in addition to meaning 'commandment' also means 'to join,' because it is the mitzvos that bind man to God.

"That is why Moses said, 'You who cling to your God, you are all alive today.' When one lives in a way that binds him to God, that bond does not disintegrate when the body dies. To the contrary, when the *neshamah* is free of the restrictions of the body, its union with God is even stronger. In that way, the righteous and just continue to live forever.

"What Luzzato is doing in *The Path of the Just* is describing the ways in which a person can elevate himself above the animal component. Without that, the human component of man is lifeless. His emphasis is on the resurrection of the living, to bring them to what is a true human life.

"When the bond between man and God is complete, which is achieved by the first nine of the ten steps, man is then resurrected. In this book, Luzzato is not discussing the physical resurrection of the dead.

"Deeds such as the one you did at the hospice bind a person to God so that one lives on eternally."

In the mail we received an announcement that Rabbi Segal was going to conduct a two-week Israel tour after Passover. I had not been to Israel for twelve years. Evelyn and I agreed we should go. I filled out the reservation form and sent in a deposit.

I had a two week interval between treatments, and we decided to take a week in Florida. I had been hesitant to be away from my doctors, but Dr. Harriman gave me the name of a doctor in Miami whom I could contact if necessary.

We were lounging on the patio of the apartment we had rented for the week, when Evelyn said, "You're different, honey, and I love it."

"Different?" I asked. "In what way?"

"It's almost noon," she said, "and you haven't even called your office once."

I laughed. "My cell phone is back home," I said. "I can check it later to see if there are any messages. I left word not to call me unless there was an extreme urgency. For heaven's sake, there are thirty-two lawyers in that office. They're more than capable of handling anything that comes along."

"When did they become all that capable?" Evelyn asked. "You weren't able to trust them last year. You had to check up on them three times a day."

"They were always capable. It was my wacky ego. I had to think that the whole firm depended on me. The world couldn't rotate if I wasn't pushing it."

"And you haven't lost your cool in a long time," Evelyn said. "That's been so nice."

"It's just that the kinds of things I used to think were of gigantic significance don't appear important enough to get steamed up about," I said.

After a few moments of silence, Evelyn said, "I went to the hospice for the first time last week. It was a mistake."

"Why?" I asked.

"Because I should have been prepared. I felt very awkward. I was introduced to a woman in her sixties. She told me that she had entered the hospice two weeks earlier. She said, 'I know I won't be going home again. I had to put my dog in a kennel. I think she misses me as much as I miss her. Her name is Bridget. She used to crawl up on my lap and snuggle up. She liked to wrap herself in my afghan.' The woman took a folded afghan from her dresser. 'If I told you the name and address of the kennel, would you take this afghan and ask them to put it in Bridget's kennel?' "

"What did you say?" I asked.

"What could I say? I said, 'Of course, I'll be glad to.' I took the afghan, and now I feel bad that I didn't have time to go to the kennel."

Evelyn continued, "I was fumbling for words. I had brought along a little bag of raspberry cookies. I gave it to her and said, 'They say that laughter and raspberry cookies are good medicine.' She smiled, tasted a cookie and said, 'Did you bake these yourself?' I couldn't lie, so I told her I had bought them. She said, 'You should bake things yourself. It's so much fun, and they taste better. Look here, if you take a pencil and paper I'll give you my secret recipe for blueberry muffins.'

"I went up to the desk and got a pencil and paper, and wrote down everything she said exactly as she said it. 'Don't let them stay in the oven a minute too long or you'll ruin them. They're the best, and you can tell everyone that these are Aunt Priscilla's muffins. I never had any children. That way there will be something to remember me by.' Then she smiled mischievously and said, 'Don't give the recipe to anyone else. Let people envy you. And when you think it's getting close for your time to go, then you give it to your daughter, alright?'

" 'You've got a deal,' I said, shaking her hand.

" 'You'll come back soon?' Priscilla asked.

" 'My husband and I are going to Florida for a week,' I said, 'but I'll come when we get back.'

" 'Don't forget,' Priscilla said. As I left, she shouted after me, 'Don't let them stay in the oven too long.'

" 'I won't,' I said."

I said to Evelyn, "Honey, you couldn't have done better if you'd taken a college course. But you might want to talk to Sherry. She's been doing this for some time. Next time you go, let's coordinate things so we go together. I want you to meet Zagermacher. He's a real character."

I couldn't help but think, here is a woman, Priscilla, who is no different than me. We're both concerned about some kind of existence after we die. Priscilla wants to be perpetuated through her secret recipe for blueberry muffins. That's better than Henry. People will enjoy Priscilla's legacy. My client Henry's legacy is an empire that his children are killing themselves over.

The day was great, and in the evening our phone rang. It

was Hadassah. "Daddy," she said, "Jason and I are getting engaged."

My first thought was, why now? Is Hadassah rushing things because she still wants me at the wedding? I said, "That's wonderful! Have you thought about setting a wedding date?" I fully expected she would say something like "two weeks from now," to assure my presence, but she said, "Not until after the summer, at least." I felt relieved. She wasn't rushing into marriage to be sure I would still be around.

Jason is a wonderful young man. He is in his residency for radiology. He comes from a fine family. His grandfather was the *chazzan* at our *shul* for years. He was the *chazzan* at my Bar-Mitzvah. He had a booming bass voice that rattled the window panes. Jason has been at our home a number of times. He is kind, considerate, and gentle. I was happy for Hadassah.

So now I want to live to walk Hadassah to the *chuppah* (wedding canopy). Strange, how I've begun to measure time, not by the calendar, but by events: the trip to Israel, Adina's baby, Hadassah's wedding, Marvin's Bar-Mitzvah.

I thought back to when I was as guilty as other people are in "killing time." Time is so precious a commodity, why kill it? I felt like shouting, "Hey, you people out there! If you have time to waste, give it to me. I need all I can get."

We weren't killing time in Florida. We were enjoying the beauty of God's world and each other's company.

When we returned home, Evelyn promptly carried out her assignment to bring the afghan to the kennel. She then said, "I've got to go back and tell Priscilla, but first I'm going to bake some blueberry muffins for her."

I thought the muffins were delicious, but Evelyn said she had to make another batch. "These are too brown. I left them in the oven too long. Priscilla will kill me."

She baked another batch and took off for the hospice. She returned aglow with pride. Priscilla had complimented her for success on her very first attempt, but added, "You can do better yet with more practice."

At a subsequent visit to the hospice, I introduced Evelyn to Zagermacher. He said to me, "I always knew you were a smart boy, but I didn't think you were so smart. You chose a good wife."

Evelyn's experience at the hospice had broken through her resistance to acceptance of my disease. On several occasions I had tried to talk to her about reality, but it was clear that she was uncomfortable, so I avoided it. But now she was more amenable. "Let's face it, honey. My first remission was seventeen months. I don't know how long this one will be. Dr. Harriman was cautiously optimistic about a new treatment that might give a longer remission, but there's no talk of a cure.

"I'm not signing off by any means, but the past two years have taught me a lot. My perspective has changed. Winning the big case is not as important as it used to be. I look forward to Adina's baby, to Hadassah's wedding, and with God's help I'll make Marvin's Bar-Mitzvah. I've come to believe that I have a mission in life, and it's not, as I thought, to have the largest Jewish law firm in the city. Whenever that mission is finished, I'll go on to what comes next.

"When Jeff and I visited Rabbi Rabinowitz, he told Jeff that the reason a child may come into the world for a short while is because that child's *neshamah* had neared its fulfillment and did not have to stay on earth very long to reach its completion. That helped Jeff, and it made me realize that I will be around as long as I have to for whatever my *neshamah* has to do. Sure, I'd like to live to one hundred, but I'm comfortable with that idea."

Evelyn said, "That's all well and good for you. What about me?"

"First things first, and please listen. You will have no financial worries. That's been taken care of. You must maintain the home. You can visit the kids and enjoy them, but never go to live with them.

"You will still be a relatively young woman, and being alone is a curse. It makes only good sense that . . .

Evelyn burst into tears. "Stop it! Stop it right now!"

"I'm sorry," I said. "I didn't mean to hurt you."

We sat in silence for a few minutes before Evelyn said,

"You talk about your mission. What's my mission? To be a court stenographer until I can collect social security?"

"We all have a function," I said, "but it's not constant. When the children were little, you diapered and fed them. When they were able to eat by themselves, you prepared their meals and washed their clothes. Then you made their lunches. We made a home for them where they could grow up to be healthy adults. Now they're independent, but Adina could share with us about the new baby, and Hadassah could tell us she's engaged to Jason. Whom would they tell it to if we weren't around? How much would Jack and Adina enjoy Marvin's Bar-Mitzvah if we weren't there, bursting with pride?

"I've often talked about Zeide and Bubby. They were very important people in my life. Parents have to discipline their children. Grandparents are there to spoil them. So I'll be a Zeide as long as I can, and you'll be a Bubby as long as you can."

"I guess your right," Evelyn said, " but I prefer that we do it together."

"Me too," I said. "Just keep praying when you light the Shabbos candles."

Evelyn received a surprise call from Rabbi Segal. His secretary had been in an automobile accident and would be out of commission for several weeks. In the meantime, arrangements for the Israel trip had to be formalized. Could she please, please come to the rescue? In several days, the secretary should be available by phone. Evelyn said she would check with me. I agreed, but told Evelyn this was taking on a massive job. There would probably be twenty-five people on the tour, which meant that she could expect repeated calls from all twenty-five, in addition to making bookings at hotels, guided tours, etc. Evelyn said that she had been thinking for some time to cut back on the job and work only as a fill-in, and this was a good opportunity to do so.

Rabbi Segal was overjoyed, and later that day dropped off a pile of brochures. He gave Evelyn a list of places the group was to visit, but from there on in, it was her decision how much time to spend at each place, where to stay, etc. Evelyn and I spent that evening looking through brochures. That was the fun part of it.

Evelyn contacted the consulate to see if a meeting could be arranged with one of the dignitaries. She spoke to several tour operators and chose one of them who became almost a member of the family. She actually had little recourse to the secretary.

Two weeks in Israel is really not that much time if you want to see everything: Jerusalem, Tel Aviv, Haifa, Eilat, Massadah, Caesera, Rosh Hanikra, Tiberias, and a kibbutz. Evelyn complicated matters by giving the tour members an option of being at a hotel on Shabbos or spending Shabbos with an Israeli family. She received the expected calls, with some people, of course, changing their minds. Some people called to find out what kind of film is best to take along, and Evelyn became an expert on photography.

She had an original idea — spending two days at Tiberias, watching sunrise from the western side of the Sea of Galilee, then going across the sea by ferry and watching the sunset from the eastern shore.

There would be, of course, a visit to the Western Wall, followed by a walk through the recently opened tunnels. More tunnels in my life!

In spite of some hassles, the tour schedule was put into final shape. Rabbi Segal could not thank Evelyn enough, and jokingly promised her a special place in heaven for this great mitzvah. As a compensation in this world, Rabbi Segal said we would not have to pay for our tour, a gesture which we appreciated but turned down.

Other than the tour arrangements, life went on as usual. We kept up our hospice visits. It was a banner day when Yonah came with one of his children to see Zagermacher. We had told him about this in advance; we were concerned that the sudden surprise of his son and grandchild walking in could precipitate a heart attack in a now eighty-six-year-old man. The hospice provided a large room for the birthday party, which was well attended by a number of Zagermacher's students. Art, Alex, and I felt we had a real mitzvah.

Evelyn took Priscilla's passing rather hard. She had formed a bond with her. For several weeks she did not go back to the hospice. Then one day she baked a triple batch of blueberry muffins and distributed them to the patients.

It's strange how the human mind works. We may be oblivious of things we do not wish to be aware of, until some crisis breaks through our denial. But as soon as things stabilize, the denial may come back.

During my seventeen-month remission, I felt fine and actually believed I was cured. My relapse made me realize this was not true. Thank God, I responded well to the second course of treatment. I did have some unpleasant side effects initially which kept me reminding me of reality, but when the course of treatment was over and I felt quite good, I again dreamed of a cure. My occasional visits to the hospice might have served as a reminder, but the ingenuity of the human mind allowed me to think, *"These* people may have an incurable disease. That's why they're in the hospice. But me? I go to the office, I drive my car, I function normally, so I'm alright. I do tire more easily, but so what? Many people tire easily."

Hadassah told us that they had set a wedding date in October. "Good," I thought. "They feel secure that I will be around in October."

We had a very pleasant Passover. We had the children and some friends for the seder. Immediately after Passover, Evelyn began finalizing the tour arrangements in earnest, because it was just two weeks to the departure date. People were calling with questions, and Evelyn sent out reminders not to forget passports. As de facto group leader, she had all the tickets.

The departure from JFK was surprisingly orderly. Once on the plane there was some grumbling about the seats, but even that subsided. We were greeted at Ben Gurion, airport by the Israeli representative of the travel agency. If you have ever retrieved your baggage from the carousels at Ben Gurion you know what an ordeal that can be. We went by chartered bus to the hotel in Jerusalem. When everyone was finally settled in their rooms with their baggage, Evelyn said, "Never again," and collapsed. I stayed awake until I reached the doctor recommended by Dr. Harriman. I introduced myself to him and told him it was my fervent hope that I would not have to bother him, but just in case there was a need, I wanted him to know who I was. Then I, too, collapsed.

The following morning Rabbi Segal took us to the Western Wall, where we prayed. I wrote my petition on a slip of paper and put it into one of the crevices. There were two festive Bar Mitzvah celebrations which we greatly enjoyed. A guide then led us through the tunnels, explaining things as we went along.

One of the things that everybody says about Jerusalem is that you can't be there without running into someone you know from back home. I indeed recognized someone at the hotel, a colleague from another city with whom I had collaborated on a case. We had become quite friendly over the years. He came to visit his daughter, who had made *aliyah* (settled in Israel) several years earlier. He happened to mention that his wife is very ill, and that he was advised to see a local rabbi for a *berachah* (blessing). I asked if he would mind if I went with him, and he said I was most welcome.

We had a free evening, so I accompanied my friend to the rabbi. We came into an anteroom crowded with people. There was one individual who was obviously in charge, and we asked him when we could see the rabbi. He said it would probably be in about an hour or so. We decided to wait.

The rabbi was a short man, with a white beard and long *peyos.* His eyes were gentle, and he greeted us warmly with a smile. He spoke Yiddish and Hebrew, so his *shamash* (aide) acted as interpreter. He asked us when we had arrived in Israel and where we were from. Inasmuch as I was a tag-along, I let my friend answer.

My friend then said that he wanted a *berachah* from the rabbi for his wife, who was suffering from advanced multiple myeloma. The rabbi said that he had heard that there may be a new treatment for multiple myeloma that should be very effective. My friend said that his wife was under the care of a leading cancer specialist, and that he was sure that they were aware of the latest advances.

The rabbi's faced changed expression. He sighed and appeared deeply affected by my friend's problem. "Remedies are provided by God, and He enlightens scientists to make new discoveries. There may soon be a discovery of a treatment that will help your wife," the rabbi said. He asked my friend for his wife's Jewish name and her mother's name. He jotted these down and said he would pray for her. "But do not rely on my prayer. You, too, must pray for her."

My friend asked the rabbi to give him a *berachah.* The rabbi said, "May you be blessed with many worries." Noting my friend's astonishment, the rabbi asked, "What is your worry now?"

"My wife's illness," my friend said.

The rabbi said, "You see, you have only one worry, because

your wife's illness dominates your entire mind. You cannot worry about anything else, because everything else seems insignificant. When your wife recovers, that major worry will be gone, and you will be able to worry about all the things that occur in life that right now appear to be trivial.

"There is no such thing as a life without worry. If you have many worries, they are all little worries. My *berachah* is that you should not have anything big to worry about."

My friend asked the *shamash* if the rabbi could give him a *shemirah*, a coin he would bless as an amulet. The rabbi explained that it is not his practice to give amulets. He said, "The coin that you will put into a *tzedakah* box is much more potent than any coin I can give you."

Seeing that my friend was finished, I took the opportunity to say, "Rabbi, I need a *berachah*. I am being treated for a disease which is presently under control, but for which there is no cure."

The rabbi asked for my name and my mother's name and jotted them down. He said, "The best treatment for any disease is *simchah* (joy). *Simchah* can stimulate the body's own healing powers. People do not have *simchah* when they worry about the future. We cannot control the future, so what is point of worrying about it? If we live each day with gratitude toward God for that day and avoid worrying about the future, we can have *simchah*. So my *berachah* to you is that you should have *simchah*."

The rabbi paused a moment and asked, "Are you anticipating any *simchos* in your family?" I told him that one daughter was expecting a baby and that my other daughter was to be married.

The rabbi's eyes lit up. "See?" he said. "God is providing you with curative *simchos*." He arose and shook our hands. My friend took out his wallet to leave some money, but the rabbi shook his head and said, "No, no. You may give money to some *tzedakah*."

When we left, my friend said, "Well, what do you make of it?"

I said, "He seems to be a very spiritual person. Did you notice that we both came with problems of a serious illness, but that his response to me was different than to you?"

My friend shrugged. "You didn't expect him to repeat himself , did you?"

Several weeks later, I received a call from my friend. "Do you remember how the rabbi kept talking to me about discovering a new treatment? Well, it has just been found that thalidomide, the drug that had caused birth defects, can be very effective in multiple myeloma. Janice is going to start thalidomide treatments next week. Do you think the rabbi could have known?"

I said, "Who knows? Maybe God does give very spiritual people some prophetic insight." I then thought that the rabbi had not predicted any new treatment discovery for me. My remedy was *simchah*, and in order to have *simchah* I must stop worrying about the future. I remembered the story Rabbi Rabinowitz had told about the rabbi who was threatened at gunpoint and who remained unperturbed, saying, "The person who has one God and two worlds is not afraid of a gun."

In the past two years I learned about an existence in another world. If I could believe this as that rabbi did, I could have *simchah*. Much of my future depended on my attitude.

I do not intend to give you a description of our fascinating tour in Israel. What surprises me is that there are so many people who have the means but have never been to Israel. Perhaps it is especially significant to me, in that it is a country whose continued existence was once thought to be hopeless. To me that is very encouraging.

I will only mention our visit to Tiberias. Evelyn's idea of watching the sunrise and sunset from the opposite shores of the Sea of Galilee was a stroke of genius. We arrived in Tiberias in the afternoon. The only thing planned was a casual tour of the city, to see the remnants of old fortress walls. Rabbi Segal took me aside and told me that Luzzato, the author of *Path of the Just*, was buried in Tiberius, and asked if I would be interested in joining him on a visit to his burial place. I seized upon the opportunity, and Evelyn and I accompanied him.

The taxi drove us up a winding road to the top of a tall hill. Rabbi Segal said that there was a tradition that Rabbi Akiva, a great Talmudic sage who was executed by the Romans for violating the ban against teaching Torah, was buried in a cave on the top of the hill. He then told us a bit about the life of Luzzato, a great person who was ruthlessly persecuted because he was falsely accused of sorcery. Luzzato wrote prolifically, especially on kabbalah. The rabbis of his time forbade him to write or teach kabbalah until he reached the age of forty, and then only in the Holy Land. He was thirty-nine when he came to the Holy Land, and died three months prior to his fortieth birthday.

Rabbi Segal led us to the cave where Rabbi Akiva is said to be buried. He had brought along a book of Psalms, and we read a few psalms there. Then we went to the nearby monument of Luzzato. At this point, I could not contain myself. I rested my head on the monument and wept. I felt a bond with this great man who had introduced me to spirituality.

We recited a psalm at Luzzato's monument. Rabbi Segal said that we should not be praying to the dead. We pray only to God. However, we pray that God be merciful to us by virtue of the many merits that these holy people had earned.

We set our alarm clocks for the following morning well ahead of sunrise. Our view of the horizon from the hotel balcony was perfect. The *Kineret* (the Hebrew name for the Sea of Galilee) was calm, like a smooth mirror. We sat with our cameras and camcorders, watching the eastern horizon brighten. Then we saw just a glimmer of gold appear on the horizon. Our cameras clicked away and our camcorders hummed as the sun slowly made its appearance.

I remembered a saying that the quantity of life is determined by how many breaths you take, but that the *quality* of life is determined by how many things take your breath away. Watching the sunrise over the *Kineret* was one such quality moment.

Our chartered bus took us around some of the scenic sights

in the Galilee. In the afternoon we boarded a ferry and crossed the *Kineret,* while our bus took the land route to the eastern shore. We checked in at a newly opened hotel, and went out to watch an exquisitely beautiful sunset. We captured these unbelievable sights with our cameras.

There is much more to tell about Israel. All I can say is, "Go and see for yourself."

W e were indeed blessed with a *simchah* when Adina delivered a beautiful baby girl.

My mother was still alive when my daughters were born. With the help of some Israeli friends, I chose the name "Adina," which means delicate, gentle, and pleasant. Hadassah was born in the week of Purim, and the rabbi suggested we call her Esther, who was the heroine of the Purim story. Evelyn had a cousin Esther whom she did not like very much, and it would have made for unpleasant associations. The rabbi said that Esther's name was also Hadassah, and that was perfect.

Inasmuch as Adina's baby was the first girl born since my mother's death, I hoped they would name her Chana Glickel. When I visited Adina in the hospital, she and Jack were discussing names. Adina must have read my mind, because she said, "Daddy, I loved Bubby very much, and I would have wanted to name the baby after her, but I can't give her the name 'Glickel.' Names like that are just not popular, and I'm afraid she'll be self-conscious. You gave me and

Hadassah beautiful Hebrew names, and we'd like the baby to have a Hebrew name, too."

I said, "Of course, honey. We'll love her just as much, whatever name she has." But I could not help but feel a pain in my heart. If Adina feels that way, Hadassah will probably feel the same way. My mother's name will not be perpetuated in the family.

This was on a Tuesday, and the naming would not be until Shabbos. Early Friday morning, Adina called me. She was at home, and asked me to stop there on my way to the office.

When I came in, Adina was all smiles. "Jack and I had pretty much settled on the name 'Tova,' which means 'good.' We thought that would be an omen that she would be good. We were going to keep part of Bubby's name and call her 'Tova Chana.'

"Last night I dreamt of Bubby. She was all smiles and said, 'Mazal Tov' to me. When I woke up, it occurred to me that 'Glickel' means 'luck' and that 'mazal' means 'luck.' I called Rabbi Segal at the shul and asked him if we could give the name 'Mazal.' Rabbi Segal said that it was a common name among Sephardic Jews. I then told him that Bubby's name was Chana Glickel, and he said that 'Chana Mazal' was the exact equivalent. So we're going to name her 'Chana Mazal,' and we're going to call her 'Mazal,' because Zeide used to call Bubby 'Glickel'."

I told Adina I was overjoyed. I kissed her and made my exit quickly because I couldn't hold back my tears. I cried out of joy and said, "Thank you, God," and "Thanks, Mom."

I felt somewhat different going to the next study session with Rabbi Segal. Being at Luzzato's tomb had impacted on me. I wondered, "How many people will cry at my grave the way I did at Luzzato's?"

Why did I cry? Because this man had made a change in my life. Granted, had I not had non-Hodgkins lymphoma, I probably would not have reacted that way. I might not even have been interested in visiting his grave, and if I did, it would not have meant that much to me. Many people read *Path of the Just,* but the first chapter on what is man's duty in this world is nothing more than an intellectual exercise to them. Most people are too busy going through the motions of life to give serious thought to why they are living. It's like they say, "You don't value something you have until you realize that you may lose it." But now that life has taken on a new value to me, I am very interested in what it's all about, and Luzzato gives me an answer.

So I wondered, "Will anyone cry at my grave?" Perhaps Evelyn, who will, at least initially, be hurting because of loneliness. My kids? I doubt it. Certainly not many years after I'm gone. It's just natural that children adjust to the loss of a parent. Why, I loved my parents dearly, but I never cry at their gravesite. I had no kinship with Luzzato, who died more than two hundred years ago. But he impacted on my life, made me rethink what I am living for, made me realize that a human being is more than *homo sapiens*, a baboon with intellect. My life was purposeful. I was given an assignment much like the alchemists of yore who tried to change lead into gold. I was given the task of transforming the "wild mule" into a spiritual being. Luzzato was helping me complete that task, and I was grateful to him. Some people cry out of pain, some out of joy. I cried out of gratitude.

And who will be grateful to me? Oh, sure, the people who I represented successfully in litigation appreciated my efforts. They paid me for my services, and that was the end of it. I seriously doubt that any of them still think, "Alan Silverman is a great person. I owe him so much." While I gave them what they wanted, I did not impact upon their lives. No one became a better person because I won their case for them.

Being a lawyer does not enhance a person's spirituality. I am hired to do the best for my client, and this does not necessarily make me a champion for truth and justice. Law is a game which you play by the rules, and if you do not violate the rules, you are not unethical. Stealing is wrong, but if you steal second base in a baseball game, you are a hero rather than a villain. If you assault someone in the street and take away his wallet, you are a thief. If you pursue someone who is running with a football, knock him down, take the football from him and run it across the goal line, you may have fifty thousand people up on their feet, cheering wildly for you. That's the way the game is played.

A client may have swindled people out of millions of dollars. If a lawyer can get him acquitted so that he can go free and keep his ill-begotten wealth, he has done an excellent job. He has stolen second base or knocked down the possessor of a football, took it from him, and ran with it for a touchdown. Those are the rules of the game, and there is nothing unethical about it. Is that truth? Hardly. Is that really justice? No way. It's the game of law.

Repeatedly doing things on a regular basis has a way of affecting a person's character. If one is not careful, the way a person acts at work may overlap into his personal life. That does not mean that lawyers are unethical in their personal lives, anymore than a baseball or football player becomes a thief. We can separate our work from our personal lives. All I'm saying is that even if our work does not detract from our spirituality, it certainly does not enhance it.

My first real exposure to spirituality was *Path of the Just*, and because of my illness, I was receptive to its teaching.

I was touched by Rabbi Segal's brief account of Luzzato's tragic life. This man was very prolific. *Path of the Just* is just one of his many works. He died before age forty, leaving an indelible impression on humanity. Here I am at fifty-six. Is the world any better because of my existence? These thoughts went through my mind after that experience in Tiberias.

Jeff, the psychologist, was amazed at Luzzato's profound understanding of the workings of the human mind. Luzzato elaborates on rationalization, how we can deceive ourselves to justify anything that we have a desire to do. We are essentially powerless to avoid rationalizing, because our desires bribe us and distort our judgment mechanism.

There is no way to avoid the pitfalls of rationalization other than having an objective person as a guide, someone who is not subject to your biases. Luzzato gives the example of people wandering through a maze, not knowing which of the many paths leads to a dead end and which leads to the goal.

There is someone standing in a high place who has a view of the maze and can see which is the path that leads to the goal. He shouts to you, "Don't go that way! That leads to a dead end. Listen to me! Follow my directions and you'll get to the goal." How foolish one would be to ignore him and to insist on finding one's way through the maze on one's own. One could spend a lifetime in aimless wandering.

I realized that I needed a guide. I am fortunate that I can turn to Rabbi Segal or to Rabbi Rabinowitz. No, I am not going to consult them on legal matters. That is not their area of expertise. But I should run my deliberations on non-work related issues by them. I resolved to do that.

Hadassah told us that Jason's parents are truly wonderful people, and are of limited means. They struggled to put Jason through medical school. There is no way that they can afford a lavish wedding, and they are very sensitive to not being able to contribute to a gala affair. They preferred a decent but rather simple wedding.

I had other ideas. After all, I am a prominent, successful attorney. I drive a Jaguar. If I have a no-frills wedding, what will people say of me? "Look at that tightwad!" I was willing to pay for all the bridesmaids' gowns, the floral arrangements, an eight-piece band, with sushi and rib-eye steaks on the menu. But if my wishes were carried out, Jason's parents would be made to feel like indigents.

I followed Luzzato's advice, and consulted Rabbi Segal. He said, "You should consider Jason's parents' feelings. If they feel hurt, it will make Jason feel badly. You don't want your children to start off their lives as a couple with negative feelings.

"What may people think of you if you have a no-frills wedding? That should not be a major concern. Too many people conduct their lives by what others will think of them rather than by what is right and proper. Certainly, you wish to be thought well of, but no one can put you down other than yourself.

"When I officiate at a marriage ceremony where many thousands of dollars are spent on flowers that will wilt in a few days, I don't think that highly of the parents who spent their money that way. Better that there should be less flowers and the money given to needy families. These are in abundance.

"Jason will respect you if you set aside your wishes in consideration of his parents' feelings. That's a good way to start a father-in-law/son-in-law relationship."

Hadassah was thrilled when I told her that we will comply with Jason's parents' wishes. Luzzato was right. Guidance from an objective person is invaluable.

Before Rosh Hashanah, I visited Rabbi Rabinowitz. I felt that on Rosh Hashanah I was submitting my application to extend my earthly visa for another year, and I wanted his blessing. Rabbi Rabinowitz invited me to join him in the succah one night.

I did just that. I took Marvin with me, because I wanted him to see what a chassidic gathering looks like.

Rabbi Rabinowitz had a huge succah, beautifully decorated. There was a large crowd there, and when he noticed me, he called me to the front. He exchanged a few words with Marvin, asking him what school he attended and what he was learning. He blessed him that he should be a source of much *nachas* (pleasure) to his parents and grandparents.

Rabbi Rabinowitz's followers sang very lively tunes, and many of them danced. He gave a discourse about the succah, much of which was over my head. He then told this fascinating story.

A certain chassidic rabbi was very poor, and all year long he saved his kopeks to be able to afford an *esrog* (citron) for the mitzvah of the four species on Succos. In Russia, an *esrog* was costly, but he managed to save enough money to buy one. Several days before Succos he took his bag of coins that he had saved and set forth to buy an *esrog*, full of joy that he would be able to fulfill a mitzvah.

On the way, he came across a man sitting at the side of the road, crying. Upon his inquiring why he was crying, the man said, "I make my living hauling things for people. My horse died this morning, and I don't have the money to buy another horse. I have a large family, and I have no way to feed them."

Without any deliberation, the rabbi took the bag of coins that he had saved all year and gave them to the man. "Here," he said, "this should help you buy another horse." The man wiped away his tears, thanked the rabbi profusely, and ran off happily.

The rabbi then turned his eyes toward heaven and said, "Master of the Universe, on Succos, Your children will be fulfilling Your mitzvah with an *esrog*. I will be fulfilling Your mitzvah with a horse."

Rabbi Rabinowitz pointed out that there were several reasons for the rabbi's action. First, he felt that the mitzvah of providing the man with the means to support his family overrode the mitzvah of *esrog*. But there was a second point. It was still several days to Succos, and the fulfillment of the mitzvah of *esrog* was not imminent. The mitzvah of *tzedakah*, however, was immediate. Rabbi Rabinowitz pointed out that one should be diligent in the performance of mitzvos, and not postpone them. When the opportunity to do a mitzvah presents itself, one should do it without hesitation.

This struck a familiar chord. In *Path of the Just* we learned that diligence in doing mitzvos is one of the steps toward spirituality.

From many angles, my life was becoming more spiritual.

My visits to the hospice were sporadic. Each time I came, Zagermacher would take out the photos of his birthday party and show me Yonah and his grandson, and those of me together with them. It was not that he did not remember. Zagermacher's memory at eighty-six was sharper than mine at fifty-six. It was just that this had been so thrilling and meaningful for him that he relived it every time he showed me the pictures.

He would say, "Alan, you had a big mitzvah." I would respond, "And for your eighty-seventh birthday, we are going to have Yonah bring one of your *great-grandchildren.*" Zagermacher would raise hands toward heaven and say, "Nu, by Gutt is everything possible."

I was blessed with another idea. Marvin was now eleven. I gave Rabbi Segal Marvin's birth date, and he was able to compute which portion of the Torah would be read at his Bar-Mitzvah. Having learned about the diligence of doing mitzvos, I thought I would implement it.

I went to Zagermacher and said, "Could you do me a

favor? I know it's a bit early, but Marvin is going to be Bar-Mitzvah in less than two years. There's no Bar-Mitzvah instructor that comes even close to you. If I brought Marvin here, could you begin to teach him his Bar-Mitzvah portion?''

Zagermacher was elated. "Sure, I can," he said. "You bring me the boy and the *haftarah* (portion of the reading from the Prophets) book, and I will teach him. Boy, will I teach him, and how! I've already had a father and son as pupils. Now I will have a grandfather and grandson. What a *mechaye* (wonderful thing)!''

I brought Marvin to Zagermacher, and he began teaching him the cantillation notes for the *haftarah*, just as he had taught me forty-four years ago. I cannot describe my joy at hearing Marvin, with his sweet voice, repeating the notes. It was a *déjà vu* phenomenon. Zagermacher said, ''He's better than you, Alan. He's very musical with a good ear. I remember you couldn't repeat after me the *kadmo-ve'azla* (one of the notes) very good. Marvin got it right on the first try.'' After he finished the session, he said to Marvin, ''You come again next week. You're gonna make a beautiful Bar-Mitzvah boy.''

I had no inkling of what I had done. Suddenly, Zagermacher felt needed. He said to me, ''How am I going to be by the Bar-Mitzvah on Shabbos? It's too far to go with the wheelchair.'' I said, ''No problem. We'll get a trailer and park it right next to the shul, and you can be there over Shabbos.'' Zagermacher was in seventh heaven, planning at eighty-six what he was going to do nearly two years later.

Hadassah's wedding was at the shul, with the dinner in the social hall rather than at a posh country club. Nevertheless, it was beautiful. The flowers were modest, and a four-piece band performed instead of eight musicians. In spite of Rabbi Segal's reassurance, I felt a bit sheepish making a wedding that was so much more austere than Adina's, but everyone appeared to be having an enjoyable time.

During the dinner, one of my wealthy clients came over to me. "I want to give you a double congratulations, Alan. First, for your daughter's marriage, and second, for having the good judgment to make a wedding that is not ostentatious. We have our daughter's wedding coming up, and my wife is going all out with elaborate preparations. I can afford it. That's not the problem, but I think that spending all that money for a five hour affair is *meschuge* (insane). When Ethel and I were married, we had a quiet ceremony with a *minyan* in the home of the rabbi. After I paid the rabbi and the *shamash*, I was broke."

I was pleased that someone felt this way, and did not realize I was being set up. My client then said, "My brother-in-law is the administrator of a project of teaching blind children in Israel. They need to expand, and I'm trying to raise some money for them. With the money you've saved on this wedding, would you make a donation? It's tax deductible."

I took out my checkbook and wrote him a sizeable check. "It's much more than tax-deductible," I said. What would have remained for Jason and Hadassah after a posh wedding? Nothing. This way, the wedding money that was saved went for a mitzvah. That's a good omen for a successful marriage.

I was very pleased with the psychologist to whom Jeff had referred me to work on my ego problem. He was very gentle, listened attentively, and responded with very insightful comments.

The discoveries I made about myself were not quite shocking, but it's just that one is generally not aware of the things that motivate a person, and how these may be both productive and counterproductive.

My father was born in a *shtetl* in Latvia, I think somewhere near Riga. The borders changed with political conquests, so I'm not sure whether this was part of Russia or Poland. He came to America with the wave of Eastern Europe immigration in 1922, when he was a young boy. Like Zagermacher, a relative who had been in America brought him over with his parents, my Zeide and Bubby. My Zeide acquired a horse and wagon and collected scrap metal and *shmattes* (rags). He sent my father to school to get an education. In Latvia it was impossible for a Jew to get an advanced education.

My father finished high school and worked odd jobs,

eventually getting a job in a garment manufacturing plant. This was in the early 1930's, during the Great Depression. In 1937 he met my mother, whose family had come from Germany, fortunately leaving during the rise of the Hitler regime. My mother's father was a doctor, from a prestigious Frankfurt family. They had been wealthy in Germany, and her father had managed to bring some money with him. He was able to set himself up in practice here.

My mother's father had the personality characteristics that are usually thought of as being typical of "yekkis" (German Jews). He was rigid, perfectionistic, and very, very proud. He was not exactly thrilled when my mother brought my father home. He had not planned for his daughter to marry a garment worker whose father came from Eastern Europe, where Jews were primitive and unenlightened, and what was worse, collected *shmattes* with a horse and wagon for a livelihood. He accepted my father with great reluctance. However, my mother loved my father very much. He deserved to be loved. He was a very warm and considerate person. Her father did not block the marriage.

My mother's father gave my father some money to open a haberdashery. That was at least more respectful than being a factory worker. I was born in 1940, when things were beginning to pick up in the economy.

Like many Jewish parents, my father had hoped I would become a doctor. This was especially important to him, because this would vindicate him in his father-in-law's eyes. Inasmuch as I would faint at the sight of blood, this was out of the question. But I knew I had to succeed at something. My father very much wanted me to be a respected professional, to offset his humble origin as the son of a peddler. From childhood on, I was driven to succeed to vindicate my father.

I excelled in school, and graduated from law school with honors. I joined a law firm, and quickly established myself as a shrewd and resourceful lawyer, which sort of satisfied my mother's father. He suggested that I open a law office of my own, and was willing to underwrite me until I had developed a clientele.

My law practice grew, and I eventually took another lawyer, Oscar Rabin, as a partner. Throughout the years we added lawyers to our firm and acquired some important corporations as clients.

My mother's father died in 1971. The psychologist pointed out that I still was trying to vindicate my father, even though his father-in-law was no longer living, and I had continued to do so even after my father died in 1977. The subconscious does not abide by logic, and although there was no one to vindicate, I was still determined to do so. Competitiveness and aggressiveness had become my lifestyle. I was driven to succeed at any cost. If I lost a case I brooded, not only because it was a personal failure, but because it meant that I had let my father down.

I was supersensitive about my image. I don't think my mother's father would have been placated had I become Chief Justice of the Supreme Court, but I tried. I had to prove that my fathers origins were not Neanderthal.

Like any normal human being, I had dependency needs, but these were anathema to me. I was power driven, and recognizing my neediness would puncture my balloon of power and independence. I learned that a lot of nutty things I had done were to avoid awareness of my neediness.

The push for power and the denial of my neediness were not good ingredients for marriage. I can look back and see that Evelyn was some kind of angel for having put up with my *shtick* (idiosyncrasies). It was only by the grace of God that I was not more frankly abusive. I had the makeup to be an abuser. I was domineering to my children. Thank God that somehow they were able to love me.

My aggressiveness in my attempt to vindicate my father was productive in terms of professional success but wreaked havoc with my personal life.

I undoubtedly would have lived the rest of my life this way, had I not been leveled by my disease. Suddenly my power had been drained away. I had to accept my mortality. I had to sit in the X-ray waiting room clad in a flimsy gown. I had to accept care from nurses who related to me as if I were in kindergarten.

Was my disease God's way of getting me to salvage my life? Was I to look upon it as a gift rather than as a punishment? That's hard to say. What I do know is that it led to another perspective on life. My interest in spirituality began to outweigh my grandiosity. I was learning how to refine my character traits.

I told my psychologist about my preoccupation with the afterlife. Was this just another manifestation of my ego wanting to survive forever and denying the possibility that I might go out of existence altogether? He didn't think so. He said that the belief in an afterlife is universal and was not mankind's way of denying human mortality. He intimated that there were many phenomena that supported the concept of an afterlife.

What was I to do about my irrational drive to vindicate my father? My psychologist said that my interest in my spiritual development had shifted my focus from my father onto myself, which was healthy. I was now trying to become the best person I could be, which was an achievable goal. Trying to vindicate the ghost of my father for the ghost of his father-in-law was a bottomless pit. The psychologist was supportive of my interest in spiritual growth, and that was very reassuring.

A s we neared the last chapter in *Path of the Just*, Rabbi Segal reminded the group of the author's instruction at the outset, that we are always at risk of regressing in spirituality, and that it is important to repeatedly review this book.

All of the steps to spirituality were major challenges, requiring a reorientation of one's lifestyle. However, the last step, that of "holiness," appeared way beyond reach. Rather than just preparing the *neshamah* for a bonding with God in the eternal world, Luzzato was now saying that our life in *this* world should be one of bonding with God. Having achieved the previous levels of spirituality, a person should be able to be essentially an angel in human form, perhaps like the angels that visited the Patriarch Abraham.

I asked Rabbi Segal whether this level was really attainable. He pointed out that Luzzato was very much aware of this objection, and that he admitted that this was not attainable by unaided human effort. However, if one did the utmost to achieve all the preceding levels of spirituality, this highest level of spirituality would be given to him "as a gift" by God.

Rabbi Segal said that there were indeed many people whose spiritual development earned them this Divine gift. He said that not only were there such saintly people in the distant past, but there were "angels on earth" even in our own time.

Rabbi Segal reminded us that his grandfather had studied under the Chafetz Chaim. "There are many stories about this great sage that testify to his having attained the level of holiness of which Luzzato speaks. The Chafetz Chaim did not live for himself. His self-effacement before God was complete. He had no will other than to do what God wanted.

"An example of his absolute detachment from self-interest is evident in this incident related by my grandfather. When the Chafetz Chaim lost a son, he was heard to say, 'Master of the Universe, I can no longer love the son You gave me. I will now direct all the love I had for him to You, and will love You more than ever.'"

Jeff winced. "Surely that is not expected of us," he said. "I still love my child dearly, nine years after she died. I cannot even conceive of detaching that love and directing it toward God,"

"Neither can I," Rabbi Segal said. "I, too, still have love for the daughter I lost. Neither you nor I are at the level of spirituality of the Chafetz Chaim. But that we are not there does not mean that we cannot reach spiritual heights.

"In the *Shema*," Rabbi Segal continued, "we declare that we are to love God with all our heart, with all our soul and with everything that we possess. The Baal Shem Tov was asked how one can achieve so absolute a love of God, since this means a total relinquishment of self-interest. The Baal Shem Tov said that the path to achieve this absolute love of God is to develop absolute love of other people. If we set our own interests aside in favor of others, that will enable us to efface ourselves before God."

"Just several years ago," Rabbi Segal said, "there was a saintly Torah scholar in Israel, Rabbi Aryeh Levin. Rabbi Levin had studied in Europe under Rabbi Isser Zalman Meltzer, who later lived in Israel.

"One day, Rabbi Levin was reminiscing with his master about his days in the yeshivah. Inasmuch as the yeshivah had no kitchen, the students were farmed out to various families in the community at whose homes they ate on assigned days. Rabbi Levin recalled at whose homes he ate during the days of the week.

"'But you did not mention at whose home you ate on Wednesdays,' Rabbi Meltzer said.

"'I had no assigned home on Wednesdays. Sometime I managed to get a snack. But not eating on Wednesdays did not bother me in the least. In fact, I did my best learning on Wednesdays.'"

"Later that night Rabbi Levin heard a knock at his door. It was Rabbi Isser Zalman's wife. 'You must come with me immediately. The rabbi is terribly agitated. I have never seen him this way before. I am actually afraid for his health.'

"Rabbi Levin promptly went to his teacher's home and found him in tears. 'Rabbi Aryeh,' he said, 'can you forgive me? Can you find it in your heart to forgive me?' Rabbi Isser Zalman said.

"Rabbi Levin was stunned. 'Me? Forgive the rabbi? For what?' he asked.

"'For having allowed you to go hungry on Wednesdays,' the master said. 'I was so absorbed with teaching and administering the yeshivah that it did not occur to me to see whether you had a place to eat every day. I was derelict in my responsibilities and I caused you to suffer.'

"'But I was fine,' Rabbi Levin said. 'I did not suffer at all.'

"'No, no,' Rabbi Isser Zalman said. 'When your parents entrusted you to me, it was my duty to see that all your needs were met. I was negligent. But perhaps you can find it in your heart to forgive me.'

" 'If the master wishes me to say that I forgive him, I will do so,' Rabbi Levin said, 'but I really do not feel there is anything to forgive.'

" 'It is not enough to say the words,' Rabbi Isser Zalman said. 'You must truly forgive me.'

" 'I truly and sincerely forgive the master with all my heart and soul,' Rabbi Levin said.

"It was only then that Rabbi Isser Zalman Meltzer felt more at ease," Rabbi Segal said. "Think of it! An incident that had happened fifty years earlier, and which Rabbi Levin did not consider to be the least bit significant, gave Rabbi Isser Zalman no peace until he felt he was genuinely forgiven.

"And we? How often do we overlook that we may have been rude to someone or have done something inconsiderate? It may not bother us in the least. If our sensitivity for others would be like that of Rabbi Isser Zalman, our self-interest would not play so great a role in our lives.

"You note that I am not describing the piety of these great men, but of their concern for others. As the Baal Shem Tov said, it is by making our personal needs secondary to the needs of others that we eliminate the obstacles that stand in the way of bonding with God. The Talmud says in *Ethics of the Fathers* that we can fulfill God's will only when we are able to set aside our own will."

"And now let me tell you about a person whom I was privileged to visit in Israel. This man was known as the Steipler Gaon. In his later years, it was difficult for him to walk. One specific Shabbos, he told his family that he had to go to a *shul* that was some distance from his home. The family tried to dissuade him because they knew that the walk would be too taxing for him, but he was adamant.

"After returning from *shul*, he explained to the family that several years earlier, he had noticed a young boy replacing a volume of the Talmud upside down in the bookcase. He had chastised him, telling him that it was disrespectful to be careless about Torah books. The youth then told him that the binder had made an error and had bound the book upside down. He had actually put it in the bookcase right side up.

"'I felt bad for having wrongly chastised the boy, and I apologized to him. Then it occurred to me that because he is before Bar-Mitzvah, he is not legally competent to forgive an insult. In halachah, competence to forgive has the same criteria as competence to transact, to buy, sell, or give. A minor lacks such competence, hence the child's acceptance of my apology did not constitute a forgiveness.

"'I had found out that today was this boy's Bar-Mitzvah. He was now competent to forgive. I had to seize the first opportunity to ask his forgiveness.'

"'Just think of it," Rabbi Segal said. "This great Torah scholar, who wrote many books on the Talmud and who corresponded with people all over the world, had for several years kept in mind that he had mistakenly chastised a child, and he waited for the opportunity to apologize to him. It is such sensitivity and concern for others that allow a person to eliminate the personal interests that stand in the way of totally subjugating himself to the will of God.

"I mentioned earlier," Rabbi Segal said, "that the Talmud explains Moses' statement 'to cleave unto God' as meaning that we are to emulate His attributes. Elsewhere the Talmud gives a second interpretation, that by cleaving unto saintly Torah scholars one cleaves unto God. The two statements are one and the same. If one follows the patterns of these Torah scholars, one indeed emulates the Divine attributes."

Jeff and I exchanged glances. "Maybe we ought to go back to Chapter One again," Jeff said.

Rabbi Segal smiled. "We all should," he said. "People like

these were not angels. They were human beings, great human beings. They had succeeded in making the care of the *neshamah* the focus of their lives. The body was appropriately cared for, but only because it was the vehicle whereby the *neshamah* could fulfill its purpose.

"What bewilders me is that so many intelligent people give so little thought to their purpose in life. Perhaps this is because they are so preoccupied with intermediate purposes that they are detracted from contemplating an ultimate purpose.

"All our actions are purposeful. We have a purpose for filling the gas tank, for going to medical school, or for putting a roast in the oven. These are indeed purposeful acts, and it may be that because we do see a purpose in our actions, we may think that we have a purpose in life."

I said to myself, "Like driving a Jaguar or building up the largest Jewish law firm."

Rabbi Segal continued, "If only people would recognize that they are mistaking intermediate purposes for an ultimate purpose, they would recognize that they are missing something.

"Let me tell you about a little incident that clarified this for me. The band on my wristwatch broke, and I did not have a chance to replace it. I put my watch in my pocket, and when I wanted to know the time, realizing that there was nothing on my wrist, I took the watch out of my pocket.

"I was sitting at my desk going through the mail. I had received a thick document held by a rubber band. I took the rubber band off and slipped it on my wrist. Thereafter, when I wanted to know the time, I did not take the watch from my pocket. Feeling there was something on my wrist, I glanced there only to discover a rubber band, which does not tell time very well.

"As long as there was nothing on my wrist, I reached into

my pocket for the watch. Once there was something on my wrist, I was deluded into thinking the watch was there."

Rabbi Segal continued, "An intermediate purpose is a poor ersatz for an ultimate purpose, just as a rubber band is a poor ersatz for a watch. But if we are preoccupied with intermediate purposes, we may be deluded to think that our lives are truly purposeful.

"That is why Luzzato emphasizes that we must detach ourselves from earthly events. We must indeed do whatever is necessarily to live normally, but we should not mistake these actions as being goals in life.

"People of great spirituality, like those I mentioned, were able to minimize their self-interest, which allowed them to be so considerate of others. This also allowed them to focus on an ultimate purpose in life."

Jeff said, "Is it realistic for us to measure ourselves according to the saintly people you described?"

Rabbi Segal responded, "I am not sure how accountable we will be held for not having achieved greater spirituality, but I am certain that we will be held accountable for not *aspiring* to greater spirituality. No, we may not become the Chafetz Chaim, but too often we resign ourselves to a level of spirituality far beneath what is attainable."

I said, "Jeff is right. We ought to go back to Chapter One."

Rabbi Segal said, "Alan, on your next trip to Israel, be sure to visit the tomb of Luzzato again. This time you may say, 'You said to review your book. I listened.'"

I was approaching the one-year mark in my second remission. Dr. Harriman had intimated that the second remission might not be as long as the first one. Although I was not panicky (I was still driving through the tunnel without any twinge of anxiety), I was apprehensive that before too long, there would be a recurrence.

I asked my psychologist if there was anything that I could do to overcome my apprehension. He said inasmuch as it was not making me dysfunctional, it was not pathologic. He discouraged my taking tranquilizers. "Tranquilizers are medications, and medicines should be used only for disease.

"What you have is not anxiety, but fear. Anxiety is when a person feels frightened without apparent reason. It is normal to be frightened if one is exposed to danger, and it is normal to feel frightened when your doctor tells you that there is no cure for your disease and that you can expect a relapse.

"What you may be able to do is learn some relaxation techniques. Fear and relaxation cannot coexist. If you can learn how to put yourself in a relaxed state, then you can quash the feelings of fear by relaxing.

"You can try to learn relaxation techniques by picking up a book on relaxation at the book store. Follow the instructions and practice frequently. If that doesn't do the trick, I can refer you to a psychologist who does biofeedback. That is an electronically mediated way of learning relaxation."

I bought a book on relaxation. Then it occurred to me that Rabbi Rabinowitz might have something to offer on the subject.

Rabbi Rabinowitz received me very warmly, as always. "*Shalom aleichem*, Reb Avraham," he said. He always called me by my Jewish name. It felt good to be in his presence. I told him of my apprehension with the occurrence of a relapse being a certainty, the only question being when. Even the hope of a new treatment was only for a longer remission. "I don't know whether I still have two, three, or four years to go."

Rabbi Rabinowitz said, "Everyone has a fear of dying. Not many people can be like the rabbi who was calm when he was threatened at gunpoint because he knew he had a second world.

"Even if one has no actual fear of death," Rabbi Rabinowitz continued, "there is nevertheless a reluctance to leave the world where we have all our loved ones. It is related that the saintly Gaon of Vilna, who certainly had a firm belief in an eternal world, wept before his death. He explained to his disciples, 'Here I am in a world where I can do mitzvos. I can give a few coins to *tzedakah*, and I can acquire a *talis* (prayer shawl) with *tzitzis* (fringes) very cheaply. In the next world, beautiful as it may be, I cannot acquire a single mitzvah even for all the gold in the world. Shall I not cry on leaving this world of opportunity to do mitzvos?'

"To saintly individuals like the Gaon of Vilna, this world is precious because of the opportunity to do mitzvos. To us ordinary people, it is precious because we have our husbands, wives, children, and grandchildren.

"But for your specific fear that the next office visit may bring you the news you dread, I suggest you say Psalm 112 every day."

Rabbi Rabinowitz took a book from his bookcase, paged through it, and began translating into English.

> *Praised be God. Fortunate is the person who reveres God, who has great delight in doing His commandments.*
>
> *His children shall be mighty on the earth; the generation of the upright shall be blessed.*
>
> *Wealth and riches shall be in his house, and his righteousness endures forever.*
>
> *For the upright, there shines a light in the darkness; he is gracious, compassionate, and righteous.*
>
> *A good man shows favor and lends; he guides his affairs with justice.*
>
> *He shall not be moved forever; the righteous shall be remembered forever.*
>
> *He shall not be afraid of evil tidings; his heart is firm with trust in God.*
>
> *His heart is firm, he shall not fear; until he sees his conquest over his tormentors.*
>
> *He has dispensed to the poor, his righteousness endures forever, his strength shall be exalted with honor.*
>
> *The wicked shall see this and be grieved; he shall gnash his teeth and melt away; the desire of the wicked shall perish.*

I felt chills going up and down my spine. I told Rabbi Rabinowitz that although this psalm had been written thousands of years ago, I felt it applied to me. "'There shines a light in the darkness,' that's my hope for the light at the end of a dark tunnel. 'To endure and be remembered forever,' that's my desire to continue to exist."

Rabbi Rabinowitz nodded. "If you can feel this psalm is for you, then you should also remember the verses, 'He shall not be afraid of evil tidings; his heart is firm with trust in God. His heart is firm, he shall not fear; until he sees conquest over his tormentors.'

"Your illness is your tormentor, and with a heart firm with trust in God, you should not fear any evil tidings. And as for your hope for light, there is the healing power of *simchah*. Light and *simchah* are intertwined. On Purim, when we celebrate our salvation from Haman's decree of extermination, we say 'for the Jews there was *orah vesimchah*, light and joy. And on Shabbos we have a beautiful Shabbos song, 'This day is *orah vesimchah*. Light and joy.'" Rabbi Rabinowitz began singing the melody of the Shabbos song, "*Orah vesimchah, orah vesimchah.*"

"I suggest you say this psalm every day. It will strengthen your trust in God and can reduce the severity of your fears. The light of *simchah* can banish the darkness of fear."

"But Shabbos and Purim are festive events. Can one be expected to have *simchah* when one confronts leaving this world?" I asked.

"Well spoken," Rabbi Rabinowitz said. "The Talmud says that a person is obligated to praise God when bad things happen as well as when good things happen, and that he must do so with *simchah*. Rashi, the foremost commentary on the Talmud, explains that in this case, *simchah* does not mean joy, but rather 'serenity.' When a person's heart is firm with trust in God, one can accept things with serenity."

Rabbi Rabinowitz gave me his blessing, and I left his study much more at ease than when I came.

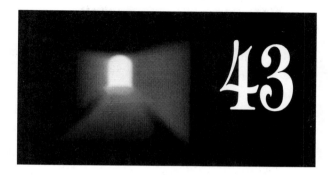

O n one visit, the nurse who usually took care of me at Dr. Harriman's office said, "Can I ask you for a favor?"

"Of course," I said.

"I attend one of the support groups of our patients," she said. "They could really use some upbeat input. I have been admiring your adjustment, and I wonder if you could come to the group and share your attitude with them."

I said, "I'd be glad to, but I really don't think I can be of much use. You see, much of my attitude is the result of a spiritual growth I've achieved, which is uniquely of Jewish theological origin. I don't think it would be of value to anyone else."

"OK," she said, "but we'd like to have you at the group anyway."

I did attend the support group, but I was a listener only. There was nothing of my experience that I could share with them.

After thirteen months into my second remission, Dr. Harriman reviewed the laboratory tests and X-rays and said, "I think it is time for a different course of treatment, Mr. Silverman. The latest tests show evidence of a relapse."

"The new treatment?" I asked.

"Yes," Dr. Harriman said. "The reports have been very favorable."

My heart sank. Dr. Harriman was going to play his trump card. Hopefully, this would provide a longer remission.

Marvin's Bar-Mitzvah was less than a year away. I was going to ask the question, but I remembered Rabbi Segal's words, "The Torah only authorizes a physician to treat. It does not authorize a doctor to set limits on how long a person can live. That is God's prerogative." I could not help thinking, "What is there to do when the next remission is over?" Perhaps in the interim, research will find an additional treatment. Many thoughts raced through my mind, but I said nothing.

Dr. Harriman said, "You are taking this very well, Mr. Silverman."

I said, "The past two and a half years have been a gift of life. When someone gives you a gift, you should be satisfied with what you get. You don't say, 'I want more.'"

"I respect your attitude very highly," Dr. Harriman said. "I don't know many people who accept things that way."

I shrugged. What could I tell him? About Succos being a joyful holiday, during which one lives in a temporary dwelling? About Chanukah, how a small flicker of light can endure and grow brighter each day? About a *neshamah* being our true essence, which is temporarily housed in a physical body, but lives on eternally? That the *neshamah* is a lamp of God? About a sage who stands up in respect for the *neshamah* of a Down Syndrome child? About a rabbi in Israel who predicted a new treatment? About a father who resolves that he will direct toward God the love he had for the son he lost? About a watchmaker's philosophy that the fear of death is really a fear of loneliness, and that if you believe that God will be with you when you walk through the valley of the shadow of death, then you will not be alone, so there is no reason to fear? About Luzzato's teaching that we are on earth to prepare ourselves for the ultimate spiritual delight of basking in the glory of God?

Dr. Harriman was indeed an excellent clinician, but he could see no light at the end of the tunnel. I was privileged to discover that there *is* a light at the end of the tunnel, a very bright light. And as Rabbi Rabinowitz said, where there is *orah* there is *simchah*. Even if not with joy, the light enables one to accept things with serenity.

Glossary

aliyah — immigrating to Israel

Amidah — Shemoneh Esrei — silent prayer

baalabus — slang for *baal habayis* — head of a household

berachah — blessing

Bubby — grandmother

chassid — pious person; following a rebbe

chazzan — cantor

chesed — kindness

chuppah — wedding canopy

dreidel — toy spinner used in Chanukah game

esrog — citron; one of the four species used on Succos

gaon — exceptional Torah scholar

Gan Eden — Paradise; Garden of Eden

gemilas chesed — acts of lovingkindness

goniff — (Yiddish) thief

haftarah — portion of Prophets read at the Shabbos service

Haggadah — narration of the Exodus from Egypt read at the Passover seder

haguf — of the body

haiske — (Yiddish) a tiny house

halachah — Torah based law

hanefesh — of the spirit

kabbalah — esoteric branch of Torah

Kaddish — prayer for the deceased

Kadmo-ve'azla — a melodic cantellation note of the Torah reading

kaftan — long robe worn by a rebbe

kiddish — 1) collation 2) prayer over wine sanctifying the Sabbath

knaidlach — matzah balls

kohen — number of the priestly tribe

L'Chaim — toast for long life

latkes — (Yiddish) pancakes

Moshiach — the Messiah

mechaye — lit. sustaining; an exclamation reflecting enjoyment and refreshment

menorah — candelabrum

meshuge — (Yiddish) insane

minyan — quorum of ten men required for prayer

mitzvah — Torah tenet

nachas — pleasure, joy

nefesh — spirit

neshamah pl. *neshamos* — soul

nu — (Yiddish) so!, Well!

Olam Haba — world to come; Paradise

orah — light

peyos — lit. ends; sidelocks

postchke — (Yiddish) putter around

rebbe — teacher, chassidic leader

refuah — healing, cure

sakanah — danger

schmaltz — rendered chicken fat

sechel — sense, intelligence

seder — festive ritual meal on Passover

segulah — something that involves good fortune

Shabbos — Sabbath

shalom — peace; greeting used both for hello and goodbye

shalom aleichem — peace be with you

shamash — beadle, sexton

shemirah — amulet

shochet — ritual slaughterer

shtetl — (Yiddish) village, hamlet

shtick — (Yiddish) idiosyncrasies

shul — synagogue

simchah — joy; joyous occasion

succah — temporary dwelling for the Succos festival

talis — prayer shawl

tamei — ritually impure

tefillin — phylacteries

Tehillim — Psalms

teshuvah — repentance

treife — non-kosher

tzaddik — righteous individual

tzedakah — alms, charity

tzitzis — lit. fringes; a fringed garment worn by males; the fringes of a prayer shawl

tzoros — troubles, woes

yahrzeit — anniversary of a death

yekki — (Yiddish) slang for one of German descent

yetzer hara — the evil inclination

yetzer tov — the positive inclination

yisgadal veyiskadash — the opening words of the Kaddish

Zeide — grandfather